KING ARTHUR & HIS KNIGHTS

CHILDREN'S
CLASSICS

KING ARTHUR & HIS KNIGHTS

Bloomsbury Books
London

This edition published 1994 by Bloomsbury Books, an
imprint of The Godfrey Cave Group, 42 Bloomsbury Street,
London, WC1B 3QJ.

ISBN 1 85471 207 1

Printed and bound by Firmin-Didot (France),
Group Herissey. No d'impression : 27258.

Contents

KING ARTHUR

The Marvel of the Sword

When Uther Pendragon, King of England, died, the country for a long while stood in great danger, for every lord who was mighty gathered his forces, and many wished to be king. For King Uther's own son, Prince Arthur, who should have succeeded him, was a child, and Merlin, the mighty magician, had hidden him away.

Now a strange thing had happened at Arthur's birth, and this was how it was.

Some time before, Merlin had done Uther a great service, on condition that the king should grant him whatever he wished for. This the king swore a solemn oath to do. Then Merlin made him promise that when his child was born, it should be delivered to Merlin to bring up as he chose, for this would be to the child's own great advantage. The king had given his promise, so he was obliged to agree. Then Merlin said he knew a true and faithful man, one of King Uther's lords, by name Sir Ector, who had large possessions in many parts of England and Wales, and that the child should be given to him to bring up.

On the night the baby was born, while it was still unchristened, King Uther commanded two knights and two ladies to take it, wrapped in a cloth of gold, and deliver it to a poor man whom they would find waiting at a gate of the castle. The poor man was Merlin in disguise, and he carried the baby to Sir Ector, and had a holy man christen him, and named him Arthur; and Sir Ector's wife looked after him as her own child.

Within two years King Uther fell gravely sick, and for three days and three nights he was speechless. All the barons were in much sorrow, and asked Merlin what could be done.

"There is no cure," said Merlin. "God will have His will. But come before King Uther tomorrow, and God will make him speak."

So the next day Merlin and all the barons came before the king, and Merlin said to King Uther: "Sire, is it your will that your son Arthur be king after you?"

Then Uther Pendragon said: "I give my son, Arthur, God's blessing and mine, and bid him pray for my soul, and righteously and honourably claim the crown, otherwise he shall forfeit my blessing." And with that, King Uther died.

But Arthur was still only a baby, and Merlin knew it would be no use yet to proclaim him king. For there were many powerful nobles in England in those days, who would try to get the kingdom for themselves, and perhaps they would kill the little prince.

There was much strife in the land for a long time, but after several years Merlin went to the Archbishop of Canterbury and counselled him to send for all the lords of the kingdom, and all the gentlemen of arms, that they should come to London at Christmas, and pray to God for a sign to show who should rightly be king. So all the lords and gentlemen came to London, and long before dawn on Christmas Day they were all gathered in the great church of St Paul's.

When the service was over, the congregation saw a strange sight in the churchyard. There was a large square stone, and in the middle of it was an anvil of steel, a foot high, and in it, stuck by the point, was a beautiful sword, and about it was written in gold these words: "He who pulls this sword out of this stone and anvil is the rightly born King of England."

When all the lords beheld the stone and the sword, they tried one after the other to pull the sword out of the stone. But not one could make it move.

"He is not here who can draw out the sword," said the archbishop, "but doubt not God will make him known. Let us provide ten knights, men of good fame, to keep guard over the sword."

So it was agreed, and proclamation was made that everyone who wished might try to win the sword. Meanwhile, the barons arranged to have a great tournament upon New Year's Day, in which all knights could take a part. They did this to keep together the lords and commons until it was made known who would win the sword.

How Arthur was Crowned King

On New Year's Day, after church, the barons rode to the field, and among them was Sir Ector, and with him rode Sir Kay, his son, with young Arthur, his foster brother.

As they rode, Sir Kay found he had lost his sword, for he had left it at his father's lodging, so he begged young Arthur to go and fetch it for him, and Arthur went gladly.

But when he came to the house, he found no one there to give him the sword, for everyone had gone to see the tournament. Then Arthur was angry and said to himself: "I will ride to the church-yard, and take the sword from the stone, for my brother shall not be without a sword today."

When he came to the churchyard, he alighted and went to seek the knights guarding the sword, but they too were all away at the tournament. So, seizing the sword by the handle, he lightly pulled it out of the stone, then took his horse and rode to join Sir Kay his brother, to whom he gave the sword.

As soon as Sir Kay saw it, he recognized the sword from the stone, so he rode to his father, Sir Ector, and said: "Sir, here is the sword of the stone. Therefore I must be king of this land."

When Sir Ector saw the sword, he took Sir Kay and Arthur back to the church, and there he made his son swear truly how he got the sword.

"My brother Arthur," said Sir Kay, "brought it to me."

"How did you get this sword ?" said Sir Ector to Arthur.

And the boy told him.

"Now," said Sir Ector, "I understand you must be king."

"Why should I be king?" said Arthur.

"Sire," said Ector, "because God will have it so, for only the man who can draw out this sword shall rightly be king. Now let me see whether you can put the sword there as it was, and pull it out again."

"That is no difficulty," said Arthur, and he put it back into the stone.

Then Sir Ector tried to pull out the sword, and failed; and Sir Kay also pulled with all his might, but it would not move.

"Now you shall try," said Sir Ector to Arthur.

"I will," said Arthur, and pulled the sword out easily.

At this Sir Ector and Sir Kay knelt down before him.

"Alas," said Arthur, "my own dear father and brother, why do you kneel to me?"

"My lord Arthur, it is not so. I was never your father, nor of your blood, but I know well you are of higher blood than I thought you were."

Then Sir Ector told him all, how he had taken him to bring up, and by whose command; and how he had received him from Merlin. And when he understood that Ector was not his father, Arthur was deeply sad.

"Will you be my good, gracious lord, when you are king?" asked Sir Ector.

"If not, I shall be to blame," said Arthur, "for you are the man to whom I am the most beholden, and your good wife, who has fostered and kept me as well as her own children. And if ever it be God's will that I be king, ask of me what I shall do, and I shall not fail you. God forbid I should fail you."

"Sire," said Sir Ector, "I will ask no more of you but that you will make my son, your foster brother Sir Kay, steward of all your lands."

"That shall be done," said Arthur, "and by my faith, never man but he shall have that office while he and I live."

Then they went to the archbishop and told him how the sword was achieved, and by whom.

On Twelfth Day all the barons came to the stone in the churchyard so that any who wished might try to pull out the sword. But none could take it out except Arthur. Many of them were very angry and said it was a great shame to them and to the country to be governed by a boy not of high blood, for as yet none of them knew that he was the son of Uther Pendragon. So they agreed to delay the decision till Candlemas, which is the second day of February.

But when Candlemas came, and Arthur once more was the only one who could pull out the sword, they put it off till Easter; and when Easter came, and Arthur again prevailed in the presence of them all, they put it off till the Feast of Pentecost.

When Pentecost came, all manner of men once more made the attempt, and once more not one of them could prevail but Arthur. Before all the lords and commons there assembled, he pulled out the sword, whereupon all the commons cried out: "We will have Arthur for our king! We see that it is God's will that he shall be our king, and he who holds against it, we will slay him."

And they knelt down, both rich and poor, and sought pardon of Arthur because they had delayed him so long.

And Arthur forgave them, and took the sword in both his hands and offered it on the altar before the archbishop, and so he was made knight by the best man there.

After that, he was crowned at once, and there he swore to his lords and commons to be a true king and to govern with true justice from thenceforth all the days of his life.

The Siege of the Strong Tower

After Arthur was crowned king, many complaints were made to him of great wrongs that had been done since the death of King Uther, many lords, knights, ladies and gentlemen having been deprived of their lands. Thereupon King Arthur caused the lands to be given again to those who owned them. When this was done, and all the districts round London were settled, he made Sir Kay steward, Sir Baldwin constable, and Sir Ulfius, chamberlain, while Sir Brastias was appointed warden of the country north of the Trent. Most of this land was then held by the king's enemies, but within a few years Arthur had won all the north.

Some parts of Wales still stood out against him, but in due time he overcame them all, as he did the rest, by the noble prowess of himself and the Knights of the Round Table.

Then King Arthur went into Wales and proclaimed a great feast, to be held at Pentecost, after his crowning in the city of Carleon. To this feast came many rich and powerful kings with great retinues of knights. Arthur was glad of their coming, for he thought that the kings and the knights had come in love and to do him honour at his feast, wherefore he rejoiced greatly and sent them rich presents.

The kings, however, would receive none of them but rebuked the messengers shamefully, saying it gave them no pleasure to receive gifts from a beardless boy of low blood They sent him word that they would have none of his gifts, but they would come and give him gifts with hard swords between the neck and the shoulders. It was for that they came hither, so they told the messengers plainly.

When the messengers brought this answer to King Arthur, by the advice of his barons he took himself with five hundred good men to a strong tower. And all the kings laid siege to him, but King Arthur had plenty of food.

Within fifteen days Merlin, the great magician, came to the city of Carleon. All the kings were very glad to see him, and asked him: "Why is that boy Arthur made your king?"

"Sirs," said Merlin, "I will tell you—it is because he is King Uther Pendragon's son. And whoever says 'Nay', Arthur shall be king and overcome all his enemies, and before he dies he shall long have been king of all England, and have under his sway Wales, Ireland, and Scotland, and more realms than I will now relate."

Some of the kings marvelled at Merlin's words and deemed it well that it should be as he said, and some of them, such as King Lot of Orkney, laughed at him, and others called him a wizard. But they all consented that King Arthur should come out and speak with them, and gave their assurance that he should come safely and should return safely.

So Merlin went to King Arthur, and told him what he had done, and bade him fear not, but come out boldly and speak with them.

"Spare them not," he said, "but answer them as their king, for you shall overcome them all, whether they will or not."

Then King Arthur came out of his tower, and there went with him the Archbishop of Canterbury, and Sir Baldwin, Sir Kay, and Sir Brastias. When he met the kings, there was no meekness but stout words on both sides, King Arthur ready with an answer to all they said and declaring that if he lived he would make them bow. They departed, therefore, very angry, and King Arthur returned to the tower and armed himself and all his knights.

"What will you do?" said Merlin to the kings. "You had better refrain, for you will not prevail here, were you ten times as many."

"Should we be afraid of a dream-reader?" sneered King Lot.

With that, Merlin vanished away and came to King Arthur, and bade him set on them fiercely. And he counselled Arthur not to fight at first with the sword he had got by miracle, but if he found himself getting the worst of the fight, then to draw it and do his best.

Meanwhile, three hundred of the best men who were with the kings, went straight over to Arthur, and this comforted him greatly. All his knights fought gallantly, and the battle raged with fury. King Arthur himself was ever in the forefront of the press, till his horse was slain underneath him. And therewith King Lot smote down King Arthur.

Four of his knights rescued him and set him on horseback. Then he drew his sword, and it was so bright in his enemies' eyes that it gave light like thirty torches; and thus he drove back his foes and slew many of them.

Then the citizens of Carleon arose with clubs and stones and slew many knights. But all the kings banded together with those of their knights who were still alive, and so fled. And Merlin came to Arthur, and counselled him to follow them no farther.

The Battle of the Kings

Then Arthur called all his barons to a council. For Merlin had told him that the six kings who had made war upon him, and whom he had defeated, would hasten to be revenged. The barons could give no counsel, but said they were big enough to fight.

"You say well," said Arthur. "I thank you for your courage, but will all of you who love me speak with Merlin? You know well that he has done much for me, and knows many things, and when he is with you I wish that you would ask him to give you his best advice."

All the barons said they would gladly hear what Merlin counselled, so the magician was sent for.

"I warn you well," said Merlin, "that your enemies are very strong, and they are as good men of arms as any alive. By this time, too, they have got to themselves four kings more, and a mighty duke, and unless our king can get more horsemen than are to be found within the bounds of his own realm, if he fights with them in battle he shall be overcome and slain."

"What is best to be done?" asked the barons.

"I will tell you my advice," said Merlin. "There are two brothers beyond the sea, and they are both kings and marvellously powerful men. One is called King Ban, of Benwick, and the other King Bors, of Gaul—that is, France. And against these two brothers wars a mighty man, the King Claudas, and strives with them for a castle; and there is great war between them. But because Claudas is very rich he gets many good knights to fight for him, and for the most part puts these two kings to the worse. Now this is my counsel—that our king and sovereign lord send to Kings Ban and Bors two trusty knights, with letters stating that if they will come and see Arthur and his court, and help him in his wars, then he will swear to help them in their wars against King Claudas. Now, what do say to this counsel?"

"This is well counselled?" said the king and the barons,
So in all haste it was settled.

Ulfius and Brastias were chosen as the messengers, and they rode forth well-horsed and well-armed, and so crossed the sea and rode towards the city of Benwick. In a narrow place they were attacked by eight knights of King Claudas, who tried to kill them or take them prisoners. But Ulfius and Brastias, fighting with them two by two, in turn overcame them all, and left them lying sorely hurt and bruised on the field.

When they came to Benwick it fortunately happened that both the kings, Ban and Bors, were there. As soon as the kings knew they were messengers of Arthur's and read the letters, the knights were made very welcome.

So Ulfius and Brastias had good cheer and rich gifts, as many as they could carry away, and they took back this answer with them— that the two kings would come to Arthur in all the haste they could.

King Arthur was very glad to get this message, and, when the time came for the kings to arrive, he proclaimed a great feast and went ten miles out of London to meet them. After the feast there was a splendid tournament in which seven hundred knights took part. Arthur, Ban, and Bors, with the Archbishop of Canterbury and Sir Ector, sat in a place covered with cloth of gold, like a hall, with ladies and gentlewomen, to behold who did best and to give judgment thereon. The knights who won the prizes were three of King Arthur's household, Sir Kay, Sir Lucas, and Sir Griflet.

With the help of King Ban and King Bors, Arthur utterly defeated the eleven kings who were warring against him. When his enemies were scattered, King Ban and King Bors, laden with rich gifts, returned to their own countries. And they made a compact with Arthur that if they had need of him to help them against King Claudas, they would send to him for help; and, on the other hand, if Arthur had need of them, he was to send, and they would not tarry.

The Knight of the Fountain

King Arthur learnt from Merlin that his mother Igraine was still alive, so he sent for her in all haste, and the queen came and brought with her Morgan le Fay, her daughter, who was as fair a lady as any might be. Igraine did not know what had become of the little babe she had entrusted to Merlin, for she had not seen the child afterwards and did not even know what name was given to him. Then Merlin took the king by the hand, saying, "This is your mother." Therewith Arthur took Queen Igraine into his arms and kissed her, and each wept over the other. Then the king commanded a feast to be held that lasted eight days.

One day there came to the court a squire on horseback, leading a knight before him, wounded to death. He told how there was a knight in the forest who had erected a pavilion by a well, and how he had slain his master, a good knight, and he sought that his master might be buried and that some knight might revenge his death.

There was much stir in the court because of this knight's death, everyone giving his advice, and a young squire called Griflet, who was about the same age as Arthur, came to the king and sought him to make him a knight.

"You are very young," said Arthur, "to take so high an order."

"Sir," said Griflet, "I beseech you to make me knight.

"Sir, it would be a great pity to lose Griflet," said Merlin, for he will be a good man when he is of age, abiding with you the term of his life."

So the king made him knight.

"Now," he said, "since I have made you knight, you must give me a gift."

"What you will," said Griflet.

Then the king made him promise that when he had fought with the knight at the fountain he would return straight to the court without further delay.

So Griflet took his horse in great haste, and got ready his shield and took a spear in his hand, and rode at a gallop till he came to the fountain. There he saw a rich pavilion, and near by under a cloth stood a fair horse, well saddled and bridled, and on a tree a shield of many colours and a great spear. Griflet struck the shield with the butt of his spear, so that the shield fell to the ground.

With that the knight came out of the pavilion and said: "Fair knight, why strike down my shield?"

"Because I would joust with you," said Griflet.

"It is better you do not," said the knight, "for you are young and lately made knight, and your might is nothing to mine."

"As for that," said Griflet, "I *will* joust with you."

"I am loath to do it," said the knight, "but since I needs must, I will make ready. From where come you?"

"Sir, I am of Arthur's court."

The two knights ran together, so that Griflet's spear was shivered to pieces, and thereupon the other knight, whose name was Pellinore, struck Griflet through the shield and left side, and broke his own spear, while horse and knight fell down.

When Pellinore saw Griflet lie so on the ground, he alighted and was very sad, for he thought he had slain him. He unlaced his helmet and gave him air, and set him again on his horse, saying he had a mighty heart, and if he lived he would prove a good knight. So Sir Griflet rode back to court, where there was great grief for him. But through good doctors he was healed and saved.

King Arthur was very angry because of the hurt to Sir Griflet, and he commanded one of his men to have his horse and armour ready waiting for him outside the city before daylight on the following morning. On the morrow, before dawn, he mounted and took spear and shield, telling the man to wait there till he returned.

He rode softly till day, and then he was aware of Merlin being chased by three churls, who would have slain him. The king rode towards them and bade them flee. They were frightened when they saw a knight, and fled.

"Oh, Merlin," said Arthur, "you would have been slain, for all your crafts, had I not been here!"

"Nay, not so," said Merlin, "for I could save myself if I would. And you are nearer your death than I am, for you are going towards your death, if God be not your friend."

As they went thus talking, they came to the fountain and the rich pavilion beside it. Then King Arthur was aware that there sat a knight, armed, in a chair.

"Sir Knight," said Arthur, "why stay you here so that no knight may ride this way unless he joust with you? I counsel you to leave that custom."

"This custom," said Pellinore, "I have used, and will use, despite who says nay; and whoever is grieved with my custom, let him mend it who will."

"I will mend it," said Arthur.

"I shall prevent you," said Pellinore.

He quickly mounted his horse, adjusted his shield, and took his spear. They met so hard against each other's shields that their spears shivered. Thereupon Arthur at once pulled out his sword.

"Nay, not so," said the knight, "it is fairer that we run once more together with sharp spears."

"I will, readily," said Arthur, "if I had any more spears."

"I have enough," said Pellinore.

A squire came and brought two good spears, and again the knight and the king spurred together with all their might, so that both the spears were broken off short. Then Arthur set hand on his sword.

"Nay," said the knight, "you shall do better. You are as good a jouster as ever I met, and for the love of the high order of knighthood let us joust once again."

"I assent," said Arthur.

Then two more great spears were brought, and each knight took one, and they ran together so that Arthur's spear was all shivered. But Pellinore hit him so hard in the middle of the shield that horse and man fell to the earth. Then Arthur eagerly pulled out his sword, saying, "I will fight you, Sir Knight, on foot, for I have lost the honour on horseback," and he ran towards him with his sword drawn.

When Pellinore saw that, he too alighted, for he thought it no honour for himself to be on horseback and the other on foot. Then began a strong battle with many great strokes till the field was wet with blood. They fought long, and rested, and then went to battle again. At last they both struck together, so that their swords met evenly, but Pellinore's sword struck Arthur's in two pieces, whereupon the king was much grieved.

Then said the knight to Arthur: "You are in danger whether I choose to save you or to slay you; and unless you yield as overcome, you shall die."

"As for death," said King Arthur, "I welcome it when it comes, but to yield to you—I had rather die than be so shamed." And with that he leapt on Pellinore, and threw him down and tore off his helmet.

The knight was very frightened, though he was a big and mighty man, but he quickly got Arthur underneath, and raised off his helmet, and would have struck off his head.

But up came Merlin and said: "Knight, hold your hand, for if you slay that knight you put this realm in the greatest damage that ever realm was in. For this knight is a man of more honour than you are aware of."

"Why, who is he?" said Pellinore.

"It is King Arthur."

Then Pellinore would have slain himself, for dread of his anger, and lifted up his sword. But Merlin cast an enchantment on the knight, so that he fell to the earth in a great sleep.

The Sword Excalibur

After throwing Pellinore into an enchanted sleep, Merlin took up King Arthur and rode forth on Pellinore's horse.

"Alas!" said Arthur, "what have you done, Merlin? Have you slain this good knight by your crafts? There lived not so worshipful a knight as he was. I would rather than a year's income that he were alive."

"Do not be troubled," said Merlin, "for he is less hurt than you. He is only asleep and will awake within three hours. There lives not a greater knight than he is, and he shall hereafter do you right good service. His name is Pellinore, and he shall have two sons, who shall be passing good men—Percival and Lamerock of Wales."

Leaving Sir Pellinore, King Arthur and Merlin went to a hermit, who was a good man and skilled in the art of healing. He attended so carefully to the king's wounds that in three days they were quite well, and Arthur was able to go on his way with Merlin. Then as they rode, Arthur said, "I have no sword."

"No matter," said Merlin, "near by is a sword that shall be yours if I can get it."

So they rode till they came to a lake, which was a fair water and broad, and in the middle of the lake, Arthur saw an arm, clothed in white silk, that held in its hand a beautiful sword. "Lo," said Merlin, "yonder is the sword I spoke of."

With that they saw a damsel rowing across the lake.

"What damsel is that?" said Arthur.

"That is the Lady of the Lake," said Merlin, "and within that lake is a rock, and therein is as fair a place as any on earth, and richly adorned. This damsel will soon come to you. Then speak fair to her, so that she will give you that sword."

Presently the damsel came to Arthur, and saluted him, and he her.

"Damsel," said Arthur, "what sword is that which yonder the arm holds above the water? I would it were mine, for I have no sword."

"Sir Arthur, King," said the damsel, "that sword is mine. The name of it is Excalibur, that is *Cut-Steel*. If you will give me a gift when I ask you, you shall have it."

"By my faith," said Arthur, "I will give you what gift you ask."

"Well," said the damsel, "go into yonder barge and row yourself to the sword, and take it and the scabbard with you, and I will ask my gift when I see my time."

So King Arthur and Merlin alighted and tied their horses to two trees, and went into the barge, and when they came to the sword that the hand held, Arthur lifted it by the handle and took it with him. And the arm and hand went under the water; and so they came to the land, and rode away.

Then King Arthur looked on the sword and liked it well.

"Which like you better, the sword or the scabbard?" asked Merlin.

"I like the sword better," replied Arthur.

"You are the more unwise," said Merlin, "for the scabbard is worth ten of the sword. While you have the scabbard upon you, you shall never lose any blood, be you never so sorely wounded. Therefore keep well the scabbard always with you."

So they returned to Carleon, where King Arthur's knights were glad to see him. When they heard of his adventures they marvelled that he would so jeopardize himself alone. But all men of honour said it was merry to be under such a chieftain who would put his person in adventures as other poor knights did.

Some time after this, Merlin again warned King Arthur to keep the scabbard of the sword Excalibur very securely, for as long as he had it upon him he would never lose any blood, however sorely he might be wounded. For greater safety, Arthur entrusted the sword and scabbard to his sister, Morgan le Fay. But Morgan le Fay was a false and treacherous woman.

She loved another knight better than her husband, King Uriens, or her brother, King Arthur, and she made up a wicked plot, by which they would both be slain. Then she meant to marry the other knight, Sir Accolon, and place him on King Arthur's throne, when she herself would become queen of the whole realm. Therefore she made by enchantment another scabbard exactly like Excalibur's, which she gave to Arthur when he was going to fight, but Excalibur and its scabbard she kept for Sir Accolon.

The Round Table

When Arthur had been king for some years, and had fought and overcome many of his enemies, his barons were anxious that he should take a wife, so according to his usual custom he went and consulted Merlin.

"It is well," said Merlin, "for a man of your wealth and nobleness should not be without a wife. Now is there any that you love more than another?"

"Yes," said King Arthur, "I love Guinevere, the daughter of King Leodegrance, of the land of Cameliard. Leodegrance holds in his house the Table Round, which he had from my father, Uther, and this damsel is the most noble and beautiful that I know living, or yet that ever I could find."

Then Merlin warned the king that it would not be wise for him to marry Guinevere. Merlin had the gift of prophecy, and knew that if this marriage took place much unhappiness would come of it. But nothing would persuade the king from his purpose. So Merlin carried a message to Leodegrance, who rejoiced greatly.

"Those are the best tidings I ever heard," he said, "that a king of prowess and nobleness will wed my daughter. And as for my lands, I would give him them if I thought it would please him, but he has lands enough, he needs none, but I shall send him a gift which shall please him much more. For I shall give him the Round Table which Uther Pendragon gave me, and when it is full complete there are a hundred knights and fifty. As for a hundred good knights, I have them myself, but I lack fifty, for so many have been slain."

So King Leodegrance delivered his daughter to Merlin, and the Round Table, with the hundred knights; and they rode briskly, with great royalty, by water and by land, till they came near to London.

When King Arthur heard of the coming of Guinevere and the hundred knights with the Round Table, he made great joy because of their coming and that rich present.

"This fair lady is welcome to me," he said, "for I have loved her long, and therefore there is nothing so dear to me. And these knights with the Round Table please me more than great riches."

Then the king commanded that preparations for the marriage be made in the most honourable way that could be devised, and he bade Merlin go forth and seek fifty knights of the greatest prowess and honour, to fill the vacant places at the Round Table.

Within a short time Merlin had found such knights as would fill twenty-eight places, but no more could he find.

Then the Archbishop of Canterbury was fetched, and he blessed the seats, and there sat the eight-and-twenty knights in their seats.

When this was done, Merlin said: "Fair sirs, you must all arise and come to King Arthur to do him homage." So they arose and did their homage.

And when they were gone, Merlin found in every seat letters of gold, that told the knight's names that had sat there, but two places were empty.

Soon after this came young Gawaine, son of King Lot of Orkney, and asked a gift of the king.

"Ask," said the king, "and I shall grant it you."

"Sir, I ask that you will make me knight the same day you shall wed Guinevere."

"I will do it with a good will," said King Arthur, "because you are my nephew, my sister's son."

So the king made Gawaine knight, and at the same time, at the wedding feast, he also knighted a son of King Pellinore, a noble and gallant youth whose name was Tor.

Then King Arthur asked Merlin why there were two places empty among the seats at the Round Table.

"Sir," said Merlin, "no men shall sit in those places, unless they be of the greatest honour. But in the Siege Perilous there shall no man sit but one, and if there be any so foolhardy to do it, he shall be destroyed; and he who shall sit there shall have no equal."

Then Merlin took King Pellinore by the hand, and leading him next the two seats and the Siege Perilous, he said: "This is your place, and best worthy are you to sit therein of those who are here."

At this, Sir Gawaine had great envy, and he said to Gaheris, his brother: "Yonder knight is given great honour, which grieves me sorely, for he slew our father, King Lot; therefore I will slay him with a sword that was sent me, which is very sharp."

You shall not do so at this time," said Gaheris, "for at present I am only a squire. When I am made knight I will be avenged on him, and therefore, brother, it is best you endure till another time, that we may have him out of the court, for if we killed him here we should trouble this high feast."

"I will do as you wish," said Gawaine.

Then was the high feast made ready, and the king was wedded to Guinevere at Camelot, in the church of St Stephen's, with great solemnity.

Then the king established all his knights, and to those who were not rich he gave lands, and charged them never to do outrage nor murders and always to flee treason. Also by no means to be cruel, but to give mercy to him that asked mercy, upon pain of forfeiture of their honour for evermore; and always to give ladies, damsels, and gentlewomen succour, upon pain of death. Also that no man should take battle in a wrongful quarrel for any law, nor for world's goods.

Thus were all the Knights of the Round Table sworn, both old and young. And every year they renewed their vows at the high Feast of Pentecost.

The Marvellous Adventure of the Magic Ship

It happened one day that Arthur and many of his knights rode hunting into a great forest. The king himself, Sir Accolon of Gaul and King Uriens, husband of Morgan le Fay, followed a fine hart, and their horses were so swift that in a little while they were ten miles ahead of their companions. Worn out with the chase, at last their horses fell exhausted, but still in front of them they saw the hart, very weary.

"What shall we do?" said King Arthur. "We are hard placed."

"Let us go on foot," said King Uriens, "till we meet with some lodging."

Then they saw that the hart lay on the bank of a large lake and the dogs had got hold of him, so King Arthur blew the "prise", which is the note blown by the hunter on the death of the quarry.

After this, he looked all around and saw before him on the lake a little ship, covered with silk down to the water, and the ship came right up to them and grounded on the sands. King Arthur went to the bank and looked in, and saw no earthly creature therein.

"Come," said the king, "let us see what is in the ship."

So they all three went in and found it richly hung with cloth of silk. By then it was dark night, and suddenly there were around them a hundred torches, set upon all the sides of the ship, which gave great light. Therewith came out twelve fair damsels, who saluted King Arthur on their knees and called him by his name, and said he was right welcome, and such cheer as they had he should have of the best. The king thanked them courteously.

The damsels led the king and his two companions into a beautiful chamber, where there was a table richly spread with all manner of good things; and here they were served with all the wines and meats they could think of, which made the king greatly marvel, for he had never fared better in his life at any one supper.

When they had supped at their leisure, King Arthur was led into another chamber, more richly adorned than he had ever seen; and so also was King Uriens served; and Sir Accolon was led into a third chamber, richly and well adorned; and so they went gladly to bed, and fell asleep at once.

But on the morrow when he awoke, King Uriens found himself in Camelot with his wife, Morgan le Fay, and this greatly astonished him, for on the evening before he was two days' journey from Camelot.

And when King Arthur awoke he found himself in a dark prison, hearing about him many complaints from woeful knights.

"Who are you that so complain?" said King Arthur.

"We are twenty knights prisoners," said they, and some of us have lain here seven years, and some more and some less.

"For what cause?" said Arthur.

"We will tell you," said the knights. "The lord of this castle is named Sir Damas, and he is the falsest knight alive, and full of treason, and the greatest coward that ever lived. He has a younger brother, a good knight of prowess, named Sir Ontzlake, and this traitor Damas, the elder brother, will give him no part of his heritage, except what Sir Ontzlake can keep through his own prowess. But the younger brother holds a fair manor, and therein he dwells in honour and is well beloved of all people, while Sir Damas is equally ill beloved, for he is without mercy and a coward. There has been great war between them, but Ontzlake always gets the better, and he keeps offering Damas to fight for the heritage, man against man, and if he will not do it himself, to find a knight to fight for him.

"To this Sir Damas agreed, but he is so hated that there is never a knight will fight for him. Seeing this, Damas has daily lain in wait with many knights and taken all the other knights in this country separately by force, as they rode on their adventures, and brought them to his prison. And many good knights, to the number of eighteen, have died in this prison from hunger. If any of us would have fought with his brother, Ontzlake, he would have released us, but because Damas is so false and so full of treason we would never fight for him. And we are so lean with hunger we can hardly stand on our feet."

"God in His mercy deliver you," said Arthur.

Just then there came a damsel to Arthur, who said: "Sir, if you will fight for my lord you shall be delivered from prison, otherwise you will never escape with life."

"Now," said Arthur, "that is hard, but I would rather fight with a knight than die in prison. On condition that I may be delivered, and all these prisoners, I will do battle. I am ready," said Arthur, "if I had horse and armour."

"You shall lack nothing," was the reply.

"It seems to me, damsel, that I have seen you in the court of Arthur."

"Nay," said the damsel, "I never went there. I am the daughter of the lord of this castle."

Yet was she false, for she was one of the damsels of Morgan le Fay.

Then she went quickly to Sir Damas and told him how Arthur would do battle for him, and so he sent for Arthur And when he came he was so handsome and well-made that all the knights who saw him said it was a pity that such a knight should die in prison.

Then Sir Damas and he agreed that he should fight for him on this covenant—that all the other knights should be released. Sir Damas swore to Arthur that this should be done, and Arthur, in return, swore to do battle to the utmost.

And with that, all the twenty knights were brought out of the dark prison into the hall and set free. And so they all waited to see the battle.

The False Craft of Morgan le Fay

Now let us turn to Sir Accolon of Gaul, who was with King Arthur and King Uriens when they went to sleep on the magic ship.

When he awoke he found himself by the side of a deep well within half a foot of the edge, in great peril of death. Out of the fountain came a pipe of silver, and out of the pipe ran water on high into a marble basin.

When Sir Accolon saw this, he said: "Heaven save my lord King Arthur and King Uriens, for these damsels in the ship have betrayed us. They were demons and not women, and if I escape this misadventure, I shall destroy, wherever I find them, all false damsels that use enchantments."

At that moment up came a dwarf with a great mouth and a flat nose, who saluted Sir Accolon and said he had come from Queen Morgan le Fay.

"She greets you well and bids you be of strong heart, for you shall fight tomorrow with a knight at the hour of noon, and therefore she has sent you here Excalibur, Arthur's sword, and the scabbard. She bids you, as you love her, that you do the battle to the utmost, without any mercy, exactly as you promised her when you spoke together in private. And the damsel who brings her the head of the knight with whom you shall fight, she will make her a queen."

"Now I understand you well," said Accolon. "I shall keep my promise now that I have the sword. Commend me unto my lady queen, and tell her all shall be done that I promised her or else I shall die for it. Now I suppose," he added, "she has made all these crafts and enchantments for this battle?"

"You may well believe it," said the dwarf.

Then up came a knight with a lady and six squires, who saluted Sir Accolon and begged him to go and rest himself at his manor. This knight was Sir Ontzlake, brother of Sir Damas, with whom King Arthur had already promised Damas to fight. So Accolon mounted a spare horse and went with the knight to a fair manor by a priory.

Sir Damas, meanwhile, had sent to his brother to bid him make ready by the next day, at the hour of noon, and to be in the field to fight with a good knight, for he had found a good knight who was ready to do battle at all points. When this word came to Sir Ontzlake he was much disturbed, for he was already wounded through both thighs with a spear, but hurt as he was he would have taken the battle in hand. But when Sir Accolon heard how Ontzlake was wounded, he said he would fight for him because Morgan le Fay had sent him Excalibur and the sheath. Then Sir Ontzlake was very glad and thanked Sir Accolon with all his heart.

The next morning when King Arthur was mounted and ready to ride forth, there came a damsel from Morgan le Fay, who brought to the king a sword like Excalibur and the scabbard, and said: "Morgan le Fay sends you here your sword for great love."

He thanked her, and thought it had been so, but she was false, for the sword and the scabbard were counterfeit, and brittle, and false.

Then King Arthur and Sir Accolon made ready, and their horses rushed so swiftly together that each struck the other with their spear's head in the middle of the shield, so that both horse and man were borne to the earth, and then both knights started up and pulled out their swords. The wicked queen had cast a spell over them so that neither knew the other. But while they were thus fighting, came the damsel of the lake, who had put Merlin under the stone, and she came for love of Arthur, for she knew how Morgan le Fay had ordained that Arthur should be slain that day; therefore Nimue came to save his life

Thus they went eagerly to the battle and gave many great strokes. But King Arthur's sword never hit like Sir Accolon's sword. Nearly every stroke that Accolon gave he sorely wounded Arthur, so that it was a marvel he stood, and always his blood fell from him fast. When Arthur saw the ground all covered with blood, he was dismayed, and guessed there was treason and that his sword had been changed. For his sword bit not steel as it was wont to do, wherefore he feared to be killed. It seemed to him that the sword in Accolon's hand was Excalibur, for at every stroke it drew blood, but he was so full of knighthood that he nobly endured the pain. And all the men who beheld him said they never saw knight fight so well as Arthur did, considering how sorely he was wounded. All the people were sorry for him, but the two brothers, Sir Damas and Sir Ontzlake, would not agree, so the knights went on fighting fiercely. Then suddenly King Arthur's sword broke at the hilt and fell in the grass, leaving the pommel and the handle in his hand. When he saw that, he greatly feared he would be killed, but always he held up his shield, and lost no ground.

How King Arthur got his own Sword Again

When Sir Accolon saw that King Arthur's sword was broken, he tried to tempt him to give in.

"Knight, you are overcome and may not endure, and also you are weaponless, and you have lost much blood. I am full loath to slay you; therefore yield to me."

"Nay," said Arthur, "I may not so, for I have promised to do battle to the utmost by the faith of my body, while life lasts, and therefore I had rather die with honour than live with shame; and if it were possible to die a hundred times, I would rather die so often than yield to you, for though I lack weapon, I shall lack no honour, and if you slay me weaponless that shall be your shame."

"Well," said Accolon, "as for the shame I will not spare. Now keep you from me, for you are but a dead man," and therewith he gave him such a stroke that he fell nearly to the earth, and he hoped Arthur would have begged for mercy.

But the king pressed forward to Accolon and gave him such a blow with the pommel of the broken sword that the knight went three strides back.

When the damsel of the lake beheld Arthur and how valorous he was, and the false treason that was wrought to have him slain, she had great pity that so good a knight and noble a man should be destroyed. And by her enchantment, at the next stroke the sword fell out of Accolon's hand to the earth. Then Arthur leaped lightly to it and got it in his hand, and immediately he knew that it was his own sword, Excalibur.

"You have been from me all too long," he cried, "and much damage have you done me."

Then he spied the scabbard hanging by Accolon's side, and he suddenly started to him and seized the scabbard, and threw it from him as far as he could.

"O Knight!" he said. "Now are you come unto your death, for I warrant you shall be as well rewarded with this sword before ever we depart, as you have rewarded me." Therewith he rushed on him with all his might, and pulled him to the ground and dashed off his helmet, and gave him such a blow on the head that it nearly killed him.

"Now will I slay you," said Arthur.

"Slay me, if it please you," said Accolon, "for you are the best knight that ever I found, and I see well that God is with you. But because I promised to do this battle to the utmost, and never to be coward while I lived, therefore shall I never yield with my mouth, but God do with my body what He will."

Then King Arthur remembered him and thought he must have seen this knight.

"Now tell me," he said, "or I will slay you, of what country are you, and of what court ?"

"Sir Knight," said Sir Accolon, "I am of the court of King Arthur, and my name is Accolon of Gaul."

Then was Arthur more dismayed than before, for he remembered his sister Morgan le Fay and the enchantment of the ship.

"O Sir Knight," he said, "I pray you tell me who gave you this sword?"

Then Sir Accolon told him how Morgan le Fay had sent it to him so that he might kill King Arthur, her brother. For King Arthur was the man in the world whom she most hated, because of his valour and renown. And if she should succeed in killing Arthur by her crafts, she would also lightly slay her husband, and then she had devised that Accolon should be king in the land and she would be queen.

"But that is now done," said Accolon, "for I am sure of my death. But now I have told you truth, I pray you tell me whence you are, and of what court ?"

"O Accolon," said Arthur, "now I let you know that I am King Arthur, to whom you have done great damage."

When Accolon heard that, he cried aloud: "Fair sweet lord, have mercy on me, for I knew you not!"

"Mercy you shall have, Sir Accolon," said Arthur, "because I see that just now you knew me not. But I understand well by your words that you have agreed to my death, and therefore you are a traitor; but I blame you the less, for my sister Morgan le Fay by her false crafts made you agree and consent to her wickedness."

Then King Arthur called the keepers of the field and told them what had happened.

"Had either of us known the other, there would have been no battle nor stroke struck," he said.

Then Sir Accolon cried aloud to all the knights and men who were there gathered, "O lords, this noble knight that I have fought with, for which I sorely repent, is the greatest man of prowess, of manhood, and of worship in the world, for it is King Arthur himself, the liege lord of us all!"

Then all the people fell down on their knees and cried mercy of King Arthur, which the king at once granted.

Then he went on to deliver judgment between the two brothers for whom he and Sir Accolon had fought. As Sir Damas was a haughty knight and full of villainy, he commanded that he should give to his younger brother the manor and all that belonged to it, and that in return Sir Ontzlake should yearly give him a horse to ride upon, for that would become him better to ride on than a charger. And on pain of death Sir Damas was evermore forbidden to distress any knights-errant who rode on adventure. And to those twenty knights whom he had so long kept prisoner he was to restore all their armour.

"And if any of them come to my court and complain of you, by my head you shall die for it," said the king. "And to you, Sir Ontzlake, because you are named a good knight, and full of prowess, and true and gentle in all your deeds, this shall be your charge: I bid you that you come to me and my court, and you shall be a knight of mine, and if your deeds be truly thus, I will so prefer you by the grace of God that you shall in a short time easily live in as much state as Sir Damas."

Then King Arthur and Sir Accolon rode to a rich abbey nearby to rest themselves and have their wounds attended to, and soon the king was well recovered. But Sir Accolon died within four days.

When Accolon was dead, the king had him sent on a horse bier, with six knights, to Camelot, and said: "Bear him to my sister, Morgan le Fay, and say that I send him to her as a present; and tell her that I have my sword Excalibur and the scabbard."

The Mantle of Precious Stones

When tidings came to Morgan le Fay that Accolon was dead and that Arthur had his sword again, she was so sorrowful that her heart was like to break. But because she would not have it known, she outwardly kept her countenance and made no sign of sorrow. But she knew well that if she remained where she was till her brother Arthur came, no gold would save her life, for he had sworn to be avenged.

She went, therefore, to Queen Guinevere and asked her leave to ride into the country.

"You can wait," said Queen Guinevere, "till your brother the king comes."

"I cannot," said Morgan le Fay, "for I have such hasty tidings that I may not tarry."

"Well," said Guinevere, "you may depart when you will."

So early on the morrow, before it was day, she took her horse and rode all that day and most of the night, and on the morrow by noon she came to the same abbey where King Arthur was. Knowing he was there, she asked how he was, and they answered that he was asleep in bed, for he had had but little rest these three nights.

"Well," she said, "I charge you that none of you awake him till I do."

Then she alighted off her horse and thought to steal away Excalibur, his sword. So she went straight to his chamber, and no man dared disobey her command, and there she found Arthur asleep on his bed, and Excalibur in his right hand, naked. When she saw that, she was greatly vexed that she could not get the sword unless she wakened him, which she knew well would be her death. So she took the scabbard and went her way on horseback.

When the king awoke and missed the scabbard, he was very angry, and he asked who had been there. They told him it was his sister, Morgan le Fay, who had put the scabbard under her mantle and was gone.

"Alas!" said Arthur, "falsely have you watched me!"

"Sir," said they all, "we dared not disobey your sister's command."

"Fetch the best horse that can be found," said the king, "and bid

Sir Ontzlake arm in all haste and take another good horse and ride with me."

So the king and Ontzlake were quickly well armed and rode after Queen Morgan le Fay. Presently they met a cowherd, whom they asked if any lady had lately ridden that way.

"Sir," said the poor man, "just now came a lady riding with forty horsemen, and she rode to yonder forest."

Then they spurred their horses and followed fast, and within a little while Arthur had a sight of Morgan le Fay; then he chased as fast as he could. When she spied him following her, she quickened her pace through the forest till she came to a plain. And when she saw she could not escape, she rode to a lake thereby and said: "Whatever becomes of me, my brother shall not have this scabbard," and she threw it into the deepest of the water so that it sank, for it was heavy with gold and precious stones.

Then she rode into a valley, where many great stones were, and seeing that she must be overtaken she shaped herself, by enchantment, into a great marble stone. When the king came, with Ontzlake, he did not know his sister and her men, nor one knight from another.

"Ah," said the king, "here you may see the vengeance of God, and now I am sorry that this misadventure is befallen."

Then he looked for the scabbard, but it could not be found. So he returned to the abbey where he came from.

When Arthur had gone, Morgan le Fay turned herself and all her knights back into the likeness that they were before, and said: "Sirs, now we may go where we will."

So she departed into the country of Gore, where she was richly received; and she made her castles and towns strong, for always she dreaded King Arthur.

After the king had well rested at the abbey, he rode to Camelot, where he found his Queen and his barons glad at his coming. When they heard of his strange adventures, they all marvelled at the falsehood of Morgan le Fay, and because of her wicked enchantments many of the knights wished her burnt.

The next day there came a damsel from Morgan to King Arthur, and she brought with her the richest mantle that ever was seen in that court, for it was set full of precious stones, and they were the richest stones that ever the king saw.

"Your sister sends you this mantle," said the damsel, "and desires that you should take this gift of her, and in what thing she has offended you she will mend it at your own pleasure."

When the king beheld the mantle it pleased him much, but he said little.

With that came the damsel of the lake to the king and said: "Sir, I must speak with you in private."

"Say what you will," said the king.

"Sir," said the damsel, "do not put this mantle on till you have seen more, and in no way let it come on you nor on any knight of yours till you command the bringer of it to put it on herself."

"Well," said King Arthur, "it shall be as you counsel me." Then he said to the damsel who came from his sister, "Damsel, this mantle that you have brought me, I will see it on you."

"Sir," said she, "it will not seemly for me to wear a king's garment."

"By my head," said Arthur, "you shall wear it before it goes on my back, or any man's who is here."

So the mantle was put on her, and immediately she fell dead and never spoke a word after, for she was burnt to a cinder.

Then was Arthur terribly angry, more than he was beforehand, and he said to King Uriens: "My sister, your wife, is always about to betray me, and well I know that either you or my nephew, your son, is in counsel with her to have me destroyed. As for you, I do not think you are in her counsel, for Accolon confessed to me with his own mouth that she would have destroyed you as well as me, therefore I hold you excused. But as for your son, Sir Uwaine, I hold him suspected, therefore I charge you put him out of my court."

So Sir Uwaine was dismissed.

When Sir Gawaine, King Lot's son, knew this, he made ready to go with him.

"Whoever banishes my cousin shall banish me," he said, so they two departed.

When Arthur was aware that Sir Gawaine had left the court, there was much sorrow among all the lords.

"Now," said Gaheris, Gawaine's brother, "we have lost two good knights for the sake of one."

SIR LANCELOT OF THE LAKE

The Strong Knight of the Forest

At the court of King Arthur were many valiant knights, and some among them increased so in arms and worship that they surpassed all their fellows in prowess and noble deeds. But chief among them all was Sir Lancelot of the Lake, for in all tournaments and jousts and deeds of arms he excelled all other knights, and never at any time was he overcome, unless it were by treason or enchantment.

Because of this, Queen Guinevere held him in higher favour than all other knights, and Sir Lancelot for his part loved the queen above all other ladies and damsels all his life; and for her he did many deeds of arms, and more than once saved her from death by his noble chivalry.

After a time at court, with many jousts and tournaments, Sir Lancelot longed again to make trial of himself in strange adventures. Therefore, bidding his nephew Sir Lionel make ready, they mounted their horses, armed at all points, and rode into a deep forest and so on to a wide plain.

About noon the weather was very hot, and Sir Lancelot felt sleepy. Then Sir Lionel spied a great apple tree that stood by a hedge, and he said: "Yonder is fair shade. There we may rest."

"It is well," answered Sir Lancelot, "for these seven years I have not been so sleepy as I am now."

So they alighted and tied their horses to a tree, and Lancelot lay down, and put his helmet under his head and fell fast asleep, but Lionel kept awake.

Then came three knights fleeing as fast as they could ride, and these three were followed by one knight. When Sir Lionel saw him he thought he had never seen so great a knight, nor so well faring a man, nor one so well apparelled. In a little while this strong knight overtook one of the three, and struck him to the cold earth, so that he lay still. Then he rode to the second knight, and struck him so that both man and horse fell down. Then he rode straight at the third knight and struck him a spear's length behind his horse's tail. Then he alighted and bound all the three knights fast with the reins of their own bridles.

When Sir Lionel saw him do this he thought he would challenge him, so making ready he took his horse very quietly in order not to awake Sir Lancelot. He soon overtook the strong knight and bade him turn, but the latter struck Sir Lionel so hard that he bore horse and man to the earth. Then he alighted and bound him fast, and threw him and the three other knights each across his own horse, and rode with them to his castle. When he got there, he took away their armour and beat them with thorns, and put them into a deep dungeon, where there were many more knights.

Sir Ector de Maris, in the meanwhile, finding that Sir Lancelot had left the court to seek adventures, was angry and made ready to go in search of him. Riding through a great forest he met a forester, and he asked him if he knew of any adventures near at hand. The forester replied that within a mile was a strong manor, with a moat all round it; and near the manor was a ford for horses to drink from. At the ford grew a beautiful tree on which hung many fair shields that had once belonged to gallant knights. On the tree hung also a basin of brass and copper, and the forester bade Sir Ector strike thrice on the basin with the butt of his spear, and he would soon hear new tidings, unless he had the greatest luck of any knight who had passed through that forest for many a year.

Thanking the man, Sir Ector departed and soon came to the tree, where he found many fair shields. Among them he saw his brother's shield, Sir Lionel's, and many more that he knew were those of his fellows of the Round Table, which grieved his heart, and he promised to revenge his brother.

He beat at once on the basin as if he were mad, and then he gave his horse drink at the ford. There came a knight behind him, and bade him come out of the water and make him ready. Sir Ector turned sharply, and cast his spear and struck the other knight a great blow, so that his horse reeled twice round.

"That was well done," said the strong knight, "and knightly have you struck me," and therewith he rushed his horse at Sir Ector, and catching him under his right arm, he bore him clean out of the saddle and rode with him away into his own hall, where he threw him down in the middle of the floor.

The name of this knight was Sir Turquine.

"Because you have done this day more to me than any knight did these twelve years," said he to Sir Ector, "now will I grant you your life, if you will swear to be my prisoner all the days of your life."

"Nay," said Sir Ector, "that I will never promise you."

"I am sorry for that," said Sir Turquine.

Then he took Sir Ector's armour away and beat him with thorns, and put him down in a deep dungeon, where he found many companions whom he knew. But when he saw Sir Lionel there he made great sorrow. "Alas," he said, "where is my brother Sir Lancelot ?"

"I left him asleep under an apple tree when I went from him," said Lionel, "and what is become of him I cannot tell you."

"Alas," said the knights, "unless Sir Lancelot help us we shall never be delivered, for we know now no knight that is able to match our master, Turquine."

The Four Queens

In the meanwhile Sir Lancelot of the Lake still lay asleep under the apple tree. Then about noon there came by four queens; and so that the heat of the sun should not annoy them there rode four knights beside them, bearing a cloth of green silk on four spears between them and the sun; and the queens rode on four white mules.

Thus as they rode they heard near them a great horse neigh, and they were aware of a sleeping knight under an apple tree; and directly these queens looked on his face they knew it was Sir Lancelot. Then they began to quarrel as to which should win his love, for each one of them said he should be her champion knight.

"Do not let us quarrel," said Morgan le Fay, King Arthur's sister, "I will put an enchantment on him that he shall not wake in six hours, and I will carry him away into my castle. And when he is safely within my hold, I will take the enchantment from him, and then let him choose which of us he shall have."

So they threw a spell over Sir Lancelot, and then they laid him on his shield and bore him so on horseback between two knights to the Castle Chariot. There he was placed in a cold chamber, and at night they sent to him a fair damsel with his supper. By that time the enchantment was past.

On the morrow early came these four queens, richly bedecked, and they bade him good morrow, and he them again. Then they told him they knew well who he was—Sir Lancelot of the Lake, King Ban's son, the noblest knight alive.

"We know well that no lady has your love but one, and that is Queen Guinevere. Now you shall lose her for ever, and she you, therefore you must now choose one of us four. I am Queen Morgan le Fay, queen of the land of Gore; and here is the queen of North Wales; and the queen of Eastland; and the queen of the Outer Isles. Now choose one of us, or else die in this prison."

"That is a hard case," said Sir Lancelot, "that either I must die or choose one of you. Yet I would rather die in this prison with honour than have one of you to be my lady against my will. And therefore you are answered. I will have none of you."

"Well," said the queens, "is this your answer, that you refuse us?"

"Yea, on my life," said Sir Lancelot, "you are refused by me."

So they departed and left him there alone in great sorrow.

At noon came the damsel to him with his dinner, and asked him, "What cheer?"

"Truly, fair damsel," said Lancelot, "in all the days of my life never so ill."

"Sir," said she, "I am sorry for that, but if you will be ruled by me I will help you out of this distress, and you shall have no shame or villainy if you will make me a promise."

"That I will grant you, and I am sore afraid of these queen sorceresses, for they have destroyed many a good knight."

Then the damsel went on to say that on the next Tuesday her father had made a tournament between himself and the king of North Wales, and if Sir Lancelot would be there to help her father she would deliver him early the next morning.

"My father is King Bagdemagus," she said, "who was defeated at the last tournament by three knights of King Arthur's court."

"I know your father well for a noble king and a good knight," said Lancelot, "and by my faith you shall have my body ready to do your father and you service at that day."

So the maiden thanked him and bade him be ready very early the next morning, and she would come and deliver him. He was to take his armour, and his horse, shield, and spear, and to ride to an abbey of white monks not ten miles away, where he was to stay, and there she would bring her father to him.

"All this shall be done," said Sir Lancelot, "as I am true knight."

The next morning Sir Lancelot rode forth into a great forest all that day. The next day he came to the abbey, where the daughter of King Bagdemagus was waiting to receive him, and before evening her father arrived with a gallant company of knights. Sir Lancelot told the king how he had been betrayed, and how his nephew Sir Lionel had departed from him; and how the king's daughter had delivered him out of prison—"therefore while I live I shall do her service, and all her kindred," he ended.

"Then am I sure of your help on Tuesday," said the king.

"Yea, sir," said Lancelot, "I shall not fail you, for so I have promised my lady, your daughter. But, sir, what knights are they of my lord Arthur's that were with the king of North Wales?"

The king replied that they were Sir Mador de la Porte, and Sir Mordred, and Sir Gahalataine, and against these three neither he nor his knights had any strength.

"Sir," said Lancelot, "as I hear say that the tournament shall be within three miles of this abbey, you shall send to me three knights of yours such as you trust, and see that the three knights have all white shields, and I also, and no painting on the shields. We four will come out of a little wood in the middle of both parties, and we will fall on the foremost of our enemies, and grieve them all we can; and thus it shall not be known what knight I am."

That night, which was the Sunday, they took their rest, and the next day King Bagdemagus departed, and he sent to Sir Lancelot the three knights with the four white shields.

The Manor by the Ford

On the Tuesday Sir Lancelot and the three knights from King Bagdemagus, with the white shields, lodged in a little leafy wood beside where the tournament would be held. And there were stands erected so that lords and ladies could see and give the prize.

Then came into the field the king of North Wales with eight score knights, and the three knights of Arthur stood by themselves.

Then came into the field King Bagdemagus with four score knights. They levelled their spears and dashed at each other, and at the first encounter twelve knights of King Bagdemagus were slain, and six of the king of North Wales, and King Bagdemagus' party was driven far back.

With that came Sir Lancelot of the Lake, and he thrust with his spear in the thickest of the press, and knight after knight went down before him, and among the throng he struck down the king of North Wales. King Arthur's three knights saw this deed of Lancelot's, and each in turn attacked him and each was vanquished.

After this he fought with twenty-eight knights, and overthrew every one of them, and then the knights of the king of North Wales would joust no more, and the prize was given to King Bagdemagus.

So each party departed to his own place, and Sir Lancelot rode forth with King Bagdemagus to his castle, where he had good cheer with the king and his daughter, and they offered him great gifts.

On the morrow he took his leave and told King Bagdemagus that he would go and seek Sir Lionel, who went from him when he was asleep. So he took his horse and commended them all to God.

So Sir Lancelot departed, and by chance he came into the same forest where he was taken sleeping. And in the middle of a highway he met a damsel riding a white horse, and they saluted each other.

"Fair damsel," said Sir Lancelot, "know you in this country any adventures?"

"Sir Knight," said the damsel, "there are adventures near at hand, if you dare prove them."

"Why should I not prove adventures?" said Sir Lancelot, "for that cause came I into the country."

"Well," said she, "you seem indeed to be a good knight, and if you dare meet with a good knight I will bring you where is to be found the best and the mightiest if you will tell me what is your name, and what knight you are."

"To tell you my name I am quite ready, truly it is Sir Lancelot of the Lake."

"Sir, you are a well-seeming knight. Here are adventures to suit you, for hereby dwells a knight who will not be matched by anyone I know, unless you match him; his name is Sir Turquine. And, as I understand, he has in his prison three score and four good knights of Arthur's court, whom he has won with his own hands. But when you have done this day's work you shall promise me, as you are a true knight, to go with me and help me and other damsels who are distressed daily by a false knight."

"I will fulfil all your desire, damsel, if you bring me to this knight."

So she brought him to the ford and to the tree where hung the basin.

Sir Lancelot let his horse drink, and then he beat with all his might on the basin with the butt of his spear, till at last the bottom fell out, but he saw nothing. He rode up and down in front of the gates of that manor for nearly half an hour. Then he was aware of a great knight coming who drove a horse before him, and across the horse lay an armed knight, bound. As they came nearer, Sir Lancelot thought he should know him, and then he saw it was Sir Gaheris, Gawaine's brother, a Knight of the Round Table.

By that time Sir Turquine had seen Lancelot, and they both gripped their spears.

"Now, fair knight," said Lancelot, "put that wounded knight off the horse and let him rest awhile, and let us two prove our strength. For, as I am told, you do, and have done, great spite and shame unto Knights of the Round Table; therefore now defend yourself!"

"If you be of the Round Table I defy you and all your fellow-ship," said Sir Turquine.

"That is saying overmuch," said Sir Lancelot.

Then they levelled their spears and came together with their horses as fast as they could run, and each struck the other in the middle of his shield, so that the two horses' backs were broken. Both knights were astonished, and as soon as they could get clear of the horses they flung their shields in front of them and drew their swords, and rushed together so eagerly that neither shields nor armour could withstand their strokes. Within a little while they had both grim wounds, and thus it fared for two hours or more. Then at the last they were both breathless, and stood leaning on their swords.

"Now, fellow," said Sir Turquine, "hold your hand awhile, and tell me what I shall ask you."

"Say on," said Lancelot.

"You are the biggest man that ever I met, and the most skilled, and like one knight that I hate above all other knights. If you are not he, then I will willingly agree with you, and for your love I will deliver all the prisoners I have, who are three score and four, so you will tell me your name. And you and I will be friends together and never fail, as long as I live."

"Well said," answered Sir Lancelot, "but since I may have your friendship, what knight is he whom you so hate above all others?"

"He is Sir Lancelot of the Lake, for he slew my brother at the Dolorous Tower, who was one of the best knights living."

"Now see I well," said Sir Lancelot, "that I might be such a man that I might have peace, and I might be such a man that there should be deadly war between us. And now, Sir Knight, at your request I desire that you know that I am Lancelot of the Lake, King Ban's son, of Benwick, and true Knight of the Table Round. And now I defy you, do your best!"

"Ah, Lancelot," said Turquine, "you are most welcome to me that ever was knight, for we shall never part till one of us be dead."

Then they hustled together like two wild bulls, rushing and lashing with their shields and swords. Thus they fought still two hours and more, and never would have rest. And Sir Turquine gave Sir Lancelot many wounds, so that all the ground where they fought was speckled with blood. Then at the last Sir Turquine waged faint, and gave somewhat aback, and bore his shield low for weariness. Sir Lancelot spied this and leaped upon him fiercely, and got him by the face piece of his helmet, and forced him onto his knees. Then he quickly raised off his helmet and struck his neck in sunder.

And when Sir Lancelot had done this, he went to the damsel, and said: "Damsel, I am ready to go with you where you will have me, but I have no horse."

"Fair sir," said she, "take this wounded knight's horse, and send him to the manor, and command him to deliver all the prisoners."

So Lancelot went to Gaheris, and prayed him not to be aggrieved at lending him his horse.

"Nay, fair lord," said Gaheris, "I will that you take my horse at your own command, for you have saved both me and my horse; and this day I say you are the best knight in the world, for you have slain here in my sight the mightiest man and the best knight, except you, that ever I saw. I pray you, sir, tell me your name.

"Sir, my name is Lancelot of the Lake, who helps you of right for King Arthur's sake, and especially for my Lord Gawaine's sake, your own dear brother. And when you come within yonder manor, I am sure you will find there many Knights of the Round Table, for I have seen many of their shields on yonder tree. And among them are my two kinsmen's shields, Sir Ector de Maris, and Sir Lionel. Wherefore I pray you, greet them all from me and say that I bid them take such treasure as they find in the manor, and that in any case let my kinsmen go to the court and wait till I come, for by the Feast of Pentecost I purpose to be there, for at this time I must ride with this damsel to keep my promise."

So Sir Lancelot departed, and Sir Gaheris went into the manor, and there he found a porter, keeping many keys. Sir Gaheris quickly threw the porter to the ground and took the keys from him, and hastily he opened the prison door and let out all the prisoners.

When they saw Gaheris they all thanked him, for they saw he was wounded.

"Not so," said Gaheris, "it was Lancelot who slew your captor, I saw it with my own eyes. And he greets you all well, and prays you to hasten to court; and as for Sir Lionel and Sir Ector de Maris, he prays you to wait for him at court."

"That shall we not do," said the brothers, "we will find him, if we live."

"So shall I find him before I go to court, as I am true knight," said Sir Kay.

Then all the knights sought the house where the armour was, and armed themselves, and every knight found his own horse, and all that belonged to him. And when this was done, there came a forester with four horses laden with fat venison.

"Here is good meat for us for one meal," said Sir Kay, "for we have had no good repast for many a day."

So the venison was roasted, baked, and boiled, and after supper some of the knights remained there in the manor all that night, but Sir Lionel and Ector de Maris and Sir Kay rode after Sir Lancelot to find him if they could.

How Sir Lancelot Slew Two Giants

Sir Lancelot rode away with the damsel, as he had promised, to aid her against the wicked knight .

"He does shame to the order of knighthood and contrary to his oath," he said. "It is pity that he lives. But, fair damsel, you shall ride on in front, and I will keep myself hidden, and if he troubles you, I will rescue you and teach him to be ruled as a knight."

So the maid rode gently along the highway. Soon out of the wood came the wicked knight on horseback, and his page with him, and he took the damsel from her horse, and she cried out.

With that came Sir Lancelot as fast as he could.

"O you false knight, and traitor to knighthood!" he said. "Who taught you to distress ladies and gentlewomen?"

When the knight heard this rebuke he made no answer, but drew his sword and rode at Sir Lancelot. Then Lancelot threw his spear from him, and drew out his sword, and struck him such a blow on the helmet that he cleaved his head and neck to the throat.

"Now you have your payment, which you have long deserved, and that is truth," said the damsel. "For as Sir Turquine watched to destroy knights, so did this knight wait to destroy and distress ladies, damsels, and gentlewomen, and his name was Sir Peris of Forest Savage."

"Now, damsel," said Sir Lancelot, "will you have any more service of me?"

"Nay, sir, not at this time," she said, "but Christ preserve you wherever you ride or go!"

And so Sir Lancelot and she parted.

Then Sir Lancelot rode into many wild and strange countries, and through many waters and valleys, and evil was he lodged. At last one night he happened by chance to come to a fair courtyard, and there he found an old gentlewoman who lodged him with a good will, and he had good cheer for himself and his horse. And when it was time, his host took him to a fair room over the gate, to go to bed. There Sir Lancelot unarmed himself, and set his armour beside him, and went to bed and quickly fell asleep.

Soon after, came one on horseback and knocked at the gate in great haste. When Sir Lancelot heard this, he arose, and looking out at the window, he saw by the moonlight three knights come riding after that one knight, and all three lashed on him at once with swords, and that one knight turned on them valiantly and defended himself.

"Truly," said Sir Lancelot, "yonder one knight shall I help, for it were shame to see three knights on one, and if he be slain, I am partner in his death."

Therewith he took his armour and went out of the window, letting himself down by a sheet, to the four knights.

"Turn, you knights, unto me!" he cried aloud, "and leave your fighting with that knight."

Then they all left the other, who was Sir Kay, and turned to Sir Lancelot, and there began a great battle, for they all three alighted and struck great strokes at Lancelot, and assailed him on every side. But when Sir Kay would have gone to Lancelot's help, the latter bade him let them fight him alone, so Sir Kay stood aside. And quickly, in six strokes, Sir Lancelot had struck them to the earth.

Then they all cried, "Sir Knight, we yield to you as a man of matchless might."

"As to that," said Sir Lancelot, "I will not take your yielding, but if you yield to Sir Kay I will save your lives, and not else."

"That we are loathe to do, fair knight," they said, "for we chased him hither and would have overcome him if you had not been here; therefore there is no reason why we should yield to him."

"As to that, be well advised," said Lancelot, "for you can choose whether you shall die or live, but if you yield, it shall be to Sir Kay."

"Well," they answered, "as you have saved our lives, we will do as you command."

Then Lancelot bade them go to the court of King Arthur on the coming Whitsunday, and there yield to Queen Guinevere, and put themselves in her grace and mercy, saying that Sir Kay had sent them to be her prisoners. And every knight swore faithfully upon his sword that he would do this. So Sir Lancelot suffered them to depart.

Then he knocked at the gate with the pommel of his sword, and there came his host, and in they entered, Sir Kay and he.

His host had heard nothing of the disturbance, and was surprised to see them. "Sir," she said, "I thought you were in your bed."

"So I was," said Sir Lancelot, "but I arose and leapt out of my window to help an old comrade of mine."

And so when they came near the light, Sir Kay knew well that it was Sir Lancelot, and he knelt down and thanked him for all his kindness, because he had this second time helped him from death.

"Sir," said Lancelot, "I have done nothing but what I ought to do, so you are welcome; and here shall you take your rest."

When Sir Kay was unarmed, he asked for some food, which was brought him, and he ate hungrily. After he had supped, he and Sir Lancelot went to their beds and lodged together in one room.

In the morning Sir Lancelot rose early and left Sir Kay sleeping, and Sir Lancelot took Sir Kay's armour and his shield, and armed himself; then he went to the stable and fetched his horse, and took leave of his host, and so he departed.

Then soon after, Sir Kay arose and missed Sir Lancelot, and then he saw that he had taken his armour and his horse.

"Now, by my faith, I know well that he will grieve some of the court of King Arthur, for knights will be bold to him, believing him to be me, and thus they will be deceived. And because of his armour and shield I am sure I shall ride in peace."

Then Sir Kay thanked his host, and soon departed.

Chapel Perilous and the Wicked Sorceress

Sir Lancelot, dressed in Sir Kay's armour, rode along in a great forest and at last he came to a flat country, full of fair rivers and meadows. Before him he saw a long bridge, and on it three pavilions of silk of different colours. Outside the pavilions hung three white shields, and great long spears stood upright by the pavilions, and at each pavilion door stood a squire. Sir Lancelot passed by these and spoke no word.

"There goes the proud Sir Kay," said the knights to whom the pavilions belonged. "He thinks no knight so good as himself, but the contrary has often been proved."

"By my faith I will challenge him, for all his pride," said one of the knights, "and you shall see how I speed." And arming himself he rode quickly after Lancelot and challenged him to fight.

But Sir Lancelot struck him down, horse and man, and after that, when the other two knights came to their brother's assistance, he overthrew them too. One of them started up with his head all bleeding and came straight to Sir Lancelot.

"Now let be," said Lancelot, "I was not far from you when you were made knight, Sir Raynold, and also I know you are a good knight, and loath I should be to slay you."

"Gramercy, as for your goodness," said Sir Raynold, "and I dare say as for me and my brethren we will not be loath to yield to you, if we knew your name, for well we know you are not Sir Kay."

"As for that, be it as it may," answered Lancelot, "for you shall yield to Queen Guinevere. Look that you be with her on Whitsunday, and yield to her as prisoners, and say that Sir Kay sent you to her."

Then they swore it should be done, and Lancelot went his way.

Riding on through the deep forest he saw in a glade four knights standing under an oak. They were all of King Arthur's court, and Sir Lancelot knew them well—they were Sagramour le Desirous, Sir Ector de Maris, Sir Gawaine, and Sir Uwaine. When they saw Lancelot they thought by his armour it was Sir Kay, so they agreed to fight him, to test his power. But Sir Lancelot rode at them all in turn, and overthrew them all, and went on his way smiling.

"What say you of this deed," said Gawaine, "that one spear has felled us four?"

"We commend him to the devil," said they all, "for he is a man of great might."

"You may well say that he is a man of might," said Gawaine, "for I dare lay my head it is Sir Lancelot. I know it by his riding. Let him go, for when we get to the court then we shall know."

Sir Lancelot rode on for a great while in the deep forest, and at last he saw a black dog seeking about as if it were tracking a hurt deer, and then he saw on the ground a trail of blood. So he rode after the dog. It went through a great marsh, and Lancelot followed, and then he saw an old manor, and thither the dog ran across a bridge. Riding over the bridge, Sir Lancelot came presently to a great hall, and in the middle he saw lying a dead knight, a noble-looking man, and the dog licked his wounds.

Then there came out a lady, weeping and wringing her hands.

"Oh, knight," she said, "too much sorrow have you brought me!"

"Why say you so?" said Sir Lancelot. "I never did this knight any harm, for hither this dog led me. Therefore, fair lady, be not displeased with me, for I am sorely grieved for your grievance."

"Truly, sir," she said, "I know it is not you who have slain my husband, for he who did the deed is sorely wounded and never likely to recover—I shall make sure of that."

"What was your husband's name ?" asked Sir Lancelot.

"Sir," said she, "he was called Sir Gilbert, one of the best knights of the world, and I know not the name of he who has slain him."

"Now God send you better comfort," said Sir Lancelot, and so he departed.

Then he went again into the forest, and there he met with a damsel who knew him well.

"Well found, my lord!" she said. "Now I require you on your knighthood to help my brother. For this day he fought with Sir Gilbert and slew him in plain battle, and there my brother was sorely wounded. And there is a lady, a sorceress, who dwells in a castle close by, and this day she told me my brother's wounds would never be whole till I could find a knight who would go into the Chapel Perilous, and there he would find a sword and a bloodstained cloth that Sir Gilbert was wrapped in; and the sword and a piece of that cloth should heal my brother's wounds."

"This is a marvellous thing," said Lancelot, "but what is your brother's name?"

"Sir," said she, "his name is Sir Meliot de Logres."

"I am sorry for that," said Lancelot, "for he is a fellow of the Round Table, and to help him I will do all in my power."

"Then, sir," said the damsel, "follow this highway, and it will bring you to the Chapel Perilous. And here I shall bide till God send you here again, and unless you succeed I know no knight living who may achieve that adventure."

So Sir Lancelot departed, and when he came to the Chapel Perilous he alighted and tied his horse to a little gate.

As soon as he was within the churchyard, he saw many rich shields, turned upside down, and many of the shields Sir Lancelot had seen knights bear formerly.

Then he saw standing there by him thirty great knights, each taller by a yard than any he had ever seen, and all these grinned and gnashed at Sir Lancelot. When he saw their countenance he was in sore dread, so he put his shield before him and took his sword in his hand, ready for battle; and all the knights were armed in black harness, ready with their shields and their swords drawn. But when Sir Lancelot would have passed through them, they scattered on every side and gave way, whereupon he waged quite bold and entered the chapel.

There he saw no light but a dim lamp burning, and then he was aware of a dead body covered with a cloth of silk.

Sir Lancelot stooped down and cut away a piece of the cloth, whereupon it seemed as if the earth quaked a little, at which he feared. Then he saw a fair sword lying by the dead knight, and he took the sword in his hand and went out of the chapel.

As soon as he was in the chapel yard all the knights spoke to him with a grim voice: "Knight, Sir Lancelot, lay that sword from you or else you shall die."

"Whether I live or die," said Lancelot, "no big words will get it again, therefore fight for it, if you choose," and so he passed through them.

Beyond the chapel yard there met him a fair damsel, who said: "Sir Lancelot, leave that sword behind you, or you will die for it."

"I shall not leave it, for any entreaties," said Lancelot.

"No," said she, "if you did leave that sword, you would never again see Queen Guinevere."

"Then I were a fool if I left it," said Lancelot.

"Now, gentle knight," said the damsel, "I require you to kiss me but once."

"Nay," said Lancelot, "God forbid!"

"Well, sir," said she, "if you had kissed me, all the days of your life would have been done. But now, alas!" she said, "I have lost all my labour, for I ordained the chapel for your sake. And now, Sir Lancelot, I tell you I have loved you these seven years, but no woman may have your love but Queen Guinevere. Since I might not rejoice to have you alive, I had no greater joy in this world than to have your body dead. Then would I have had it embalmed and preserved, and so have kept it all the days of my life, and daily I would have kissed you, in spite of Queen Guinevere."

"You say well," said Sir Lancelot. "God preserve me from your subtle crafts!"

And then he took his horse and departed from her.

And when Sir Lancelot departed she took such sorrow that she died within a fortnight, and her name was Hellawes, the sorceress, lady of the Castle Nigramous.

Sir Lancelot soon met with the damsel, Sir Meliot's sister, and when she saw him, she clapped her hands and wept for joy, and then they rode to a castle near by where Sir Meliot lay.

But Sir Meliot was as pale as death from bleeding; then Lancelot sprang to him, and touched his wounds with Sir Gilbert's sword and wiped them with a piece of the cloth in which Sir Gilbert had been wrapped, and immediately Sir Meliot was more well and strong than he had ever been in his life.

Then there was great joy between them, and they made Sir Lancelot all the cheer they could. When Sir Lancelot took his leave in the morning, he bade Sir Meliot go to the court of King Arthur, for it drew nigh to the Feast of Pentecost, and there by the grace of God he would find him.

Two days before the Feast of Pentecost he went home, and the king, and all the court rejoiced greatly at his coming. When the four knights with whom he had fought in the wood saw Sir Lancelot in Kay's armour they knew well it was he who had struck them all down with one spear, and there was much laughing and smiling among them. And now all the knights whom Sir Turquine had kept as prisoners came trooping home, and they all honoured and worshipped Sir Lancelot. When Sir Gaheris heard them speak, he said, "I saw all the battle, from the beginning to the end," and there he told King Arthur how it was, and how Sir Turquine was the strongest knight that ever he saw, except Sir Lancelot; and there were nearly three score knights who bore him record.

Then Sir Kay told the king how Sir Lancelot had rescued him when he would have been slain in the night, and how he made the knights yield to Sir Kay and not to himself. And there the knights were, all three.

"And by my faith," said Sir Kay, "because Sir Lancelot took my harness and left me his, I rode in good peace, and no man would touch me."

Then also came the three knights who fought with Lancelot at the long bridge, and they would have yielded at the court to Sir Kay, but Sir Kay refused them and said he never fought with them.

"But I will ease your hearts," he said. "Yonder is Sir Lancelot, who overcame you."

When they knew that, they were glad.

Then Sir Meliot de Logres came home and told King Arthur how Sir Lancelot had saved him from death by facing the unknown dangers and the evil spells in the Chapel Perilous.

And all his deeds were known—how four queens, sorceresses, had him in prison, and how he was delivered by King Bagdemagus's daughter. Also there were told all the great deeds of arms that Sir Lancelot did in the tournament between the two kings, that is to say, the king of North Wales and King Bagdemagus.

So at that time Sir Lancelot had the greatest name of any knight of the world, and he was the most honoured, both by high and low.

THE KITCHEN KNIGHT

The Three Gifts

Once when King Arthur held his Round Table in its full glory, it happened that he commanded that the high Feast of Pentecost should be held at a castle in a city which in those days was called Kink-Kenadon, upon the sands that marched next Wales. The king had always a special custom at the Feast of Pentecost—namely, that he would not sit down to meat until he had heard of, or seen, a great marvel. And because of this custom all manner of strange adventures came before Arthur at that feast, more than at any other festival in the year.

On this day of Pentecost, a little before noon, Sir Gawaine saw from a window three men on horseback and a dwarf on foot. The three men alighted, and the dwarf kept their horses, and one of the three men was taller than the other two by a foot and a half.

Then Sir Gawaine went to the king, and said: "Sire, go to your meat, for here at hand come strange adventures."

So Arthur went to meat with many other kings, and all the Knights of the Round Table were there, save those who were prisoners or who had been slain in battle. For at the high feast the whole number of one hundred and fifty should always be present, for then was the Round Table fully complete.

Then came into the hall two men, richly clad, with the goodliest young man and the fairest that they had ever seen leaning on their shoulders, as if he could not go by himself. He was large and tall, and broad in the shoulders, handsome of face, and had the largest and most beautiful hands that ever a man saw.

As soon as King Arthur saw him, place and room were made, and the two strange men went with him right up to the high dais without saying a word.

Then this great young man pulled himself back, and easily stretched up straight, saying: "King Arthur, God bless you and all your fair fellowship, and especially the fellowship of the Round Table. And for this I am come hither, to pray you and require you to

49

give me three gifts, and they shall not be unreasonably asked, but such as you may honourably grant to me, at no great hurt or loss. The first gift I will ask now, and the other two gifts I will ask this day twelvemonth, wherever you hold your high feast."

"Now ask," said Arthur, "and you shall have your asking."

"Sir, this is my petition for this feast—that you will give me meat and drink sufficient for this twelvemonth, and at that day I will ask my other two gifts."

"My fair son," said Arthur, "ask better, I counsel you, for this is but a simple asking; my heart assures me greatly that you are come of men of worship, and much my judgment fails me unless you prove a man of right good worship."

"Sire," said the young man, "let that be as it may, I have asked that which I will ask."

"Well," said the king, "you shall have meat and drink enough, I never forbade that to any one, either my friend or my foe. But what is your name?"

"I cannot tell you."

"That is a marvel, that you know not your name," said the king. "You are the goodliest young man that ever I saw." And he went to Sir Kay, the steward, and charged him that he should give the stranger lad all manner of meat and drinks of the best, and that he should be provided for in every way as if he were a lord's son.

"There is little need to spend so much on him," said Sir Kay, "for I dare undertake he is of mean birth, and will never make a man; if he had come of gentle folk he would have asked of you horse and armour, but he asks according to his own nature. And since he has no name I will give him one—*Beaumains*, that is, 'Fairhands'— and I will bring him into the kitchen, and there he shall have rich broth every day, so that by the twelve months' end he shall be as fat as a pork hog."

So the two strange men departed, leaving the tall lad to Sir Kay, who scorned and mocked him.

Sir Gawaine and Sir Lancelot were very angry at the way in which Sir Kay treated the lad, but the steward persisted he would never make a man of worship, because he only desired meat and drink. He bade him get a place and sit down to meat, so Beaumains went to the hall door, and sat down among the serving boys and lads, and there he ate sadly.

After the meal Sir Lancelot bade him come to his chamber, and there he should have meat and drink enough, and Sir Gawaine offered the same. But he refused them both. He would do nothing but what Sir Kay commanded him.

As for Sir Gawaine, it was natural he should offer Beaumains lodging, with meat and drink, for the boy was nearer kin to him than he guessed. But what Sir Lancelot did was of his great gentleness and courtesy.

So Beaumains was put into the kitchens, and lay nightly as the boys of the kitchen did. And he endured it all a twelvemonth, and never displeased man or child, but was always meek and mild. But if ever there were any jousting of knights, he would see it if he could. Sir Lancelot and Sir Gawaine often gave him gold to spend, and clothes. Wherever there were any feats of skill and strength, there Beaumains would be, and no one could cast bar or stone as he did, by two yards. Then Sir Kay would say: "How like you my kitchen knight?"

So time passed till the feast of Whitsuntide came round again.

And that year the king held it at Carleon in most royal fashion. But on Whitsunday, according to his custom, he would eat no meat until he heard some adventure. Then there came a squire to the king, and said, "Sir, you may go to meat, for here comes a damsel with some adventures," whereupon the king was glad, and sat down.

At that moment a damsel came into the hall, and saluted the king, and prayed succour of him.

"For whom," said the king. "What is the adventure?"

"Sir," said she, "I have a lady of great worship and renown, and she is besieged by a tyrant so that she cannot get out of her castle. And because in this your court are the noblest knights of the world, I come to pray succour of you."

"What is your lady called, and where dwells she? And who is he, and what is his name, who has besieged her?"

"Sir King," said the damsel, "as for my lady's name, that you shall not know from me at present, but on my word she is a lady of great worship, and of many lands. As for the tyrant who besieges her and destroys her lands, he is called the Red Knight of the Red Lawns."

"I know him not," said the king.

"Sir," said Gawaine, "I know him well, for he is one of the most dangerous knights in the world. Men say that he has seven men's strength, and from him I escaped once full hardly with my life."

"Fair damsel," said the king, "there are knights here who would do their utmost to rescue your lady, but because you will not tell her name, nor where she dwells, therefore by my will none of my knights that are now here shall go with you."

"Then I must seek further," said the damsel.

As she said these words Beaumains came before the king, and spoke: "Sir King, God thank you, I have been these twelve months in your kitchen, and have had my full sustenance, and now I will ask my two gifts that are left."

"Ask," said the king.

"Sir, these shall be my two gifts. First, that you will grant me to have this adventure of the damsel, for it belongs to me."

"You shall have it," said the king, "I grant it."

"Then, sir, this is the other gift, that you shall bid Lancelot of the Lake make me knight, for of him I will be made knight, or else of none. Therefore when I am gone I pray you let him ride after me, and make me knight when I require him."

"All this shall be done," said the king.

"Fie on thee!" said the damsel. "Shall I have none but one that is your kitchen page?"

Then she took her horse, in great wrath, and departed.

The Scornful Damsel

Then came a messenger to Beaumains and told him that his horse and armour had come, and that the dwarf was there with everything he needed, in the richest style. All the court marvelled greatly where such beautiful array came from. When he was armed there were few indeed who looked so good as he.

Thus he came into the hall, and took his leave of King Arthur, and Sir Gawaine, and Sir Lancelot; and begging the latter to follow after him, he departed and rode after the damsel.

Many followed him to behold how well he was horsed, and trapped in cloth of gold, but he had neither shield nor spear. Then Sir Kay said all openly in the hall: "I will ride after my kitchen knight, to find out whether he will know me for his better."

Sir Lancelot and Sir Gawaine said, "You had best abide at home." But Sir Kay made ready and took horse and spear, and rode after Beaumains.

Just as Beaumains overtook the damsel, up came Sir Kay.

"Beaumains! What, sir, do you not know me?" he cried.

Beaumains turned his horse, and knew it was Sir Kay, who had always treated him with scorn.

"Yes," he said, "I know you for an ungentle knight of the court, and therefore, beware of me."

Then Sir Kay levelled his spear and ran straight at him, and Beaumains, sword in hand, came equally fast against Sir Kay. With his sword he dashed away Sir Kay's spear and thrust him in the side so that he fell down as if he were dead. Then Beaumains alighted and took Sir Kay's shield and spear, and bidding his dwarf mount Sir Kay's horse, he sprang upon his own horse and rode away.

Sir Lancelot saw all that had happened, and so did the damsel, and Sir Lancelot having by this time come up to them, Beaumains offered to joust with him.

They came together so fiercely that each bore down the other to the earth, and sorely were they bruised. Then Lancelot arose and helped Beaumains to get free from his horse. Throwing his shield from him, Beaumains offered to fight with Sir Lancelot on foot. They rushed together like boars, tracing, racing, and thrusting, for the whole of an hour, and Sir Lancelot marvelled at the strength of Beaumains, for he fought more like a giant than a knight, and his fighting was steady and very dangerous.

Sir Lancelot had such to hold his own that he dreaded being disgraced.

"Beaumains," he said, "fight not so sore, your quarrel and mine is not so great but we may leave off."

"Truly that is truth," said Beaumains, "but it does me good to feel your might; and yet, my lord, I did not show my utmost strength."

"Well," said Sir Lancelot, "I swear to you that I had as much as I could do to save myself from you unshamed, therefore have no doubt of any earthly knight."

"Do you hope that I may ever at any time stand a proved knight?" said Beaumains.

"Yes," said Lancelot, "do as you have done, and I will be your warrant."

"Then I pray you give me the order of knighthood."

"Well, you must tell me your name and of what kin you are born."

"Sir, if you will not reveal it, I will."

"Nay," said Lancelot, "and that I promise you by the faith of my body, until it be openly known."

"Then, sir, my name is Gareth," said Beaumains, "and I am the brother of Sir Gawaine, by the same father and mother."

"Now I am more than ever rejoiced," said Lancelot, "for I always thought you must be of noble race, and that you came not to the court either for meat or drink."

And then Sir Lancelot gave him the order of knighthood.

After this, Lancelot left Beaumains and went to Sir Kay, and had him carried home on his shield. Sir Kay barely escaped with his life, and all men scorned him, and especially Sir Gawaine; and Sir Lancelot said it was not his part to rebuke any young man when he knew little of what birth he came from and for what cause he came to court.

In the meanwhile Beaumains had overtaken the damsel, but as soon as he came near she cried rudely: "What are you doing here? You smell of the kitchen! Your clothes reek of the grease and tallow that you gained in King Arthur's kitchen. Do you suppose I will accept you because of yonder knight you killed? Nay, truly, for you slew him by ill chance and cowardly. Therefore turn back, vile kitchen page! I know you well, for Sir Kay named you Beaumains. What are you but a clumsy fellow, and a turner of spits, and a ladle-washer?"

"Damsel," replied Beaumains, "say to me what you will. I will not go from you, whatever you say, for I have undertaken to King Arthur to achieve your adventure. I shall finish it to the end, or I shall die for it."

"Fie on thee, kitchen knave! Will you finish my adventure? You will meet one whom, for all the broth that ever you supped, you would not once look in the face."

"I'll try," said Beaumains.

As they rode thus in the forest there came a man fleeing as fast as he could.

"Oh, lord," he said, "help me, for hard by in a glade are six robbers who have taken my lord and bound him. I am afraid lest they slay him."

"Take me there," said Beaumains.

So they went together till they came to where the knight was bound, and then Sir Beaumains rode at the robbers, and struck one unto death, and then another, and at the third stroke he slew the third robber; and then the other three fled. Beaumains rode after them and overtook them, whereupon they all assailed him hard, but at last he slew them, and returned and unbound the knight.

The knight thanked him and prayed him to ride with him to his castle a little way off, and he would reward him honourably for his good deeds.

"Sir," said Beaumains, "I will have no reward. This day I was made knight of noble Sir Lancelot, and therefore I will have no reward, except God reward me. And also I must follow this damsel."

But when he came near she bade him ride at a distance.

"You smell of the kitchen!" she said scornfully. "Do you think I am glad to have you? For this deed you have done is nothing but chance. You shall soon see a sight that will make you turn again, and that briskly!"

Then the same knight who had been rescued from the robbers rode after the damsel and begged her to lodge with him that evening. And because it was near night the damsel rode with him to his castle, and there they were made very welcome.

At supper the knight placed Beaumains above the damsel.

"Fie, fie, Sir Knight!" she said. "You are uncourteous to set a kitchen page above me! He is better fitting to kill a pig than to sit above a lady of high parentage."

The knight was ashamed at her rude words, and taking Beaumains he placed him at a side table, and sat down himself beside him.

They had good cheer, and rested well that night.

The Black Knight of the Black Lawns

On the morrow the damsel and Beaumains, thanking the knight, took their leave and rode on their way until they came to a great forest. Here there was a great river, and but one passage, and two knights were ready on the further side to stop their crossing.

"What say you?" said the damsel. "Will you match yonder knights or turn again?"

"Nay," said Sir Beaumains, "I will not turn again if there were six more."

Thereupon he rushed into the water, and one of the knights did the same. They fought in the middle of the river, and Beaumains smote the knight on the helmet, so that he fell down into the water and was drowned. Then Beaumains spurred his horse to the further side of the river, where the other knight fell upon him and broke his spear, and so they drew their swords and fought long together. But at last Beaumains cleaved his head and his helmet down to the shoulders.

Then he went back to the damsel and bade her ride forth on her way.

"Alas," she said, "that ever a kitchen page should have the fortune to destroy two such doughty knights! You imagine you have done valiantly! That is not so. As for the first knight, his horse stumbled, and there he was drowned in the water—it was never by your strength nor your might. And the last knight, by mishap you came behind him, and by evil luck you slew him."

"Damsel," said Beaumains, "you may say what you will, but with whomever I have to do I trust to God to vanquish him before he departs, and therefore I care not what you say, if only I may reach your lady."

"Fie, fie, kitchen knave! You shall see knights who shall abate thy boast!"

"Fair damsel, give me goodly language, and then I mind nothing; for what knights whoever they be I care not, neither do I fear them."

"I say it for your own sake," she said, "that you may yet turn back with triumph; for if you follow me you are but slain, for I see that all you ever do is but by misadventure, and not by prowess."

"Well, damsel, you may say what you will, but wherever you go, I will follow you."

So Beaumains rode with the lady until evensong time, and ever she chided him and would not rest. Then they came to a black lawn, where there was a black hawthorn; thereon hung a black banner, and on the other side hung a black shield; by the tree stood a black spear, great and long, and a great black horse covered with silk, and a black stone fast by.

There sat a knight all armed in black harness, and his name was the Knight of the Black Lawn.

When the damsel saw the knight, she bade Beaumains flee down the valley, for the black horse was not saddled.

"Thanks," said Beaumains, "for always you would have me a coward!"

With that, the Black Knight, when she came near him, spoke and said: "Damsel, have you brought this knight of King Arthur to be your champion?"

"Nay, fair knight," said she, "this is but a kitchen knave, who was fed in King Arthur's kitchen for alms."

"Why comes he in such array?" said the knight. "It is shame that he bears you company."

"Sir, I cannot be delivered from him," she said, "for with me he rides, in spite of all I can do. Would that you would put him from me, or else slay him if you can, for he is an unhappy knave, and unhappily he has done this day. Through mishap I saw him slay two knights at the passage of the water; and other deeds he did before, right marvellous, and through ill fortune."

"It astonishes me that any man who is of worship will have to do with him," said the knight.

"They know him not," replied the damsel, "and because he rides with me they think he is some man of high birth."

"That may be," said the Black Knight. "Howbeit as you say he is no man of worship, he is a right goodly person, and full like to be a strong man. But this much I will grant you," he continued; "I shall put him down on foot, and his horse and his harness he shall leave with me, for it were shame to me to do him any more harm."

When Sir Beaumains heard him say this, he said: "Sir Knight, you are full liberal of my horse and my harness. I let you know it cost you nothing, and whether it likes you or not, this lawn will I pass, in spite of you. And horse or harness get you none of me unless you win them with your hands; and therefore let see what you can do!"

"Say you that?" said the Black Knight. "Now yield the lady, for it is not seemly for a kitchen page to ride with such a lady."

"You lie," said Beaumains; "I am a gentleman born, and of more high lineage than you, and that I will prove on your body."

Then in great wrath they drew apart their horses, and came together as if it had been thunder; and the Black Knight's spear broke, and Beaumains thrust him through both his sides, and his spear broke, and the truncheon was left still in his side. Nevertheless the Black Knight drew his sword, and struck many eager strokes and of great might, and hurt Beaumains full sore. But at the last, within an hour and a half, the Black Knight fell down off his horse in a swoon, and there he died.

Beaumains, seeing him so well horsed and armed, alighted and armed himself in his armour, and taking his horse he rode after the damsel. When she saw him come near she cried: "Away, kitchen knave, out of the wind, for the smell of your greasy clothes grieves me! Alas," she said, "that ever such a knave as you are should by mishap slay so good a knight as you have done, but all this is your evil luck! But hereby is one who shall pay you all your payment, and therefore still I counsel your—flee!"

"It may happen me to be beaten or slain," said Beaumains, "but I warn you, fair damsel, I will not flee away nor leave your company for all that you can say. You are for ever declaring they will kill me or beat me, but however it happens, I escape, and they lie on the ground. And therefore it were good for you to hold still, thus all day rebuking me, for I will not go away till I see the very end of this journey, unless I am slain, or truly beaten. Therefore ride on your way, for follow you I will, whatever happen."

So they took their horses and rode to his manor, which was hard by.

The Scornful Damsel grows Kind

Within a little while they saw a tower as white as snow, having a double moat, and the parapets of the walls well provided with holes for hurling stones or pouring molten lead on the heads of any foes who might besiege it. Over the tower gate hung fifty shields of divers colours, and under the tower was a fair meadow. In the meadow were many knights and squires looking after scaffolds and pavilions, for on the morrow was to be a great tournament there.

The lord of the castle was called the Red Knight, and he was the brother of the Black Knight.

When he saw Beaumains, he came forth to fight with him, but after a furious struggle Beaumains vanquished him. He declared he would only spare his life at the request of the scornful damsel, so unwillingly she had to beg mercy for him. Then the Red Knight did homage to Sir Beaumains, and offered him his fealty at all times, he and his three score knights, to do him service and bidding whenever and wherever he commanded.

That night Beaumains and the damsel lodged in the castle of the Red Knight, and the next morning they went on their way.

But all this time the scornful damsel kept scolding and rebuking Beaumains in the rudest manner.

"Damsel," said Beaumains, "you are uncourteous to rebuke me as you do, for it seems to me I have done you good service; you keep on threatening me I shall be beaten by knights whom we meet, but ever, for all your boast, they lie in the dust or in the mire; therefore, I pray you, rebuke me no more. When you see me beaten or yielding as a coward, then you may bid me go from you in disgrace; but first I let you know I will not depart from you, for I were worse than fool if I went when all the time I am winning honour."

"Well," said she, "right soon you shall meet a knight who will pay you all your wages, for he is the man of greatest renown in the world, except King Arthur."

"I wish nothing better," said Beaumains. "The more renowned he is, the more it shall be to my renown to have to do with him."

Then they were soon aware of a rich and beautiful city before them, and between them and the city for the space of a mile and a half stretched a fair meadow, that seemed newly mown, and therein were many pavilions, splendid to see.

"Lo," said the damsel, "yonder is a lord who owns yonder city, and it is his custom when the weather is fair to live in this meadow to joust and tourney; and he has always about him five hundred knights and gentlemen of arms, and there are all manner of games that any gentleman can devise."

"I would fain see that goodly lord," said Beaumains.

"You shall see him in time enough," said the damsel; and just then, as they rode near, she spied the pavilion where he was. "Lo," said she, "see you yonder pavilion that is of the colour of Inde— dark blue? And everything that is about, men and women, and horses with trappings, shields and spears, all the colour of Inde? His name is Sir Persant of Inde, the lordliest knight that ever you looked on."

"It may well be," said Beaumains, "but be he never so stout a knight, in this field I shall abide till I see him under his shield."

"Ah, fool, you had better flee betimes."

"Why?" said Beaumains. "If he be such a knight as you make him, he will not set upon me with all his men, or with his five hundred knights. For if there come no more but one at a time, I shall not fail him, while my life lasts."

"Fie, fie," said the damsel, "that ever a kitchen knave should utter such a boast!"

"Damsel," he said, "you are to blame thus to rebuke me, for I would rather fight five battles than thus to be rebuked. Let him come, and then let him do his worst."

"Sir," she said, "I marvel of what kin you are come; boldly you speak, and boldly have you done, that have I seen. Therefore I pray you save yourself if you can, for your horse and you have had great travail, and I dread we stay overlong from the siege, for it is but seven miles hence. And we are past all perilous passages, save only this passage; and here I sorely dread lest you shall catch some hurt. Therefore I would you were hence, that you may not be bruised by this strong knight. But I tell you, this Sir Persant of Inde is nothing of might nor strength to the knight who laid the siege against my lady."

"As for that," said Beaumains, "be it as it may, for since I have come so nigh this knight I will prove his might before I depart from him, else I shall be shamed if I now withdraw. Therefore, damsel, doubt not that by the grace of God I shall so deal with this knight that within two hours after noon I shall be free from him, and then we shall come to the siege by daylight."

"Oh, indeed I marvel what manner of man you be," said the damsel, "for it cannot be otherwise than that you come of noble blood, for so rude and shamefully did never woman rule a knight as I have done you, and ever courteously you have suffered me, and that never came but of gentle blood."

"Damsel," said Beaumains, "a knight can do little that cannot suffer a woman. Whatever you said to me I took no heed to your words, for the more you said, the more you angered me, and my wrath I wreaked upon those with whom I had to do withal. Therefore all the unseemly words you spoke furthered me in my battle, and caused me to resolve to show and prove myself what in the end I was; for peradventure, though I had meat in King Arthur's kitchen, yet I might have had meat enough in other places. But all this I did to prove and assay my friends, and that shall be known another day. Whether I be a gentleman born or none, fair damsel, I have done you gentleman's service, and peradventure better service will I yet do before I depart from you."

"Alas," she said, "fair Beaumains, forgive me all I have said or done against you."

"With all my heart I forgive it you," he said, "for you did nothing but as you should do, for all your evil words pleased me. And, damsel, since you speak thus fairly to me, know well it gladdens my heart greatly, and now it seems to me there is no knight living but I am able enough for him."

By this time Sir Persant of Inde had seen them as they hovered in the field, and knightly sent to ask whether they came in war or peace. To this Beaumains replied that was exactly as Sir Persant pleased, whereupon Sir Persant said he would fight with him to the utmost. So he armed himself and rode against him. Long and fierce was the encounter, but in the end Beaumains was the victor; Sir Persant surrendered and asked for mercy. The damsel, too, came and prayed for his life, which Beaumains granted right willingly, "For it were pity this noble knight should die," he said.

Then Sir Persant knew it was Beaumains who slew his brother the Black Knight at the black thorn, and who had also overcome his brother the Red Knight, Sir Perimones. And he said Beaumains should have homage and fealty of him and a hundred knights, to be always at his command, to go and ride wherever he should command them.

So they went to Sir Persant's pavilion and drank wine and ate spices.

The next morning when the damsel and Beaumains were taking their leave Sir Persant asked whither they were going.

"Sir," said the damsel, "this knight is going to the siege that besieges my sister in the Castle Perilous."

"Ah, ah," said Persant, "that is the Knight of the Red Lawns, who is the most dangerous knight that know now living, and a man that is without mercy; and men say that he has seven men's strength. God save you from that knight," he said to Beaumains, "for he does great wrong to that lady. She is one of the fairest ladies of the world, and your damsel, I think, is her sister. Is not your name Linet?"

"Yes, sir, and my lady sister's name is Dame Liones."

"Now I will tell you," said Sir Persant, "this Red Knight of the Red Lawns has lain well-nigh two years at siege; and many times he might have captured the lady, but he prolonged the time, hoping to have Sir Lancelot of the Lake to do battle with him, or Sir Tristram, or Sir Lamorak of Wales, or Sir Gawaine; and this is his reason for tarrying so long at the siege."

"Now, my lord Sir Persant of Inde," said Linet, "I require that you will make this gentleman knight before ever he fight with the Red Knight."

"I will, with all my heart," said Sir Persant, "if it please him to take the order of knighthood from so simple a man as I am."

"Sir," said Beaumains, "I thank you for your good will. I am well sped, for truly the noble knight Sir Lancelot made me knight."

"Ah," said Persant, "of a more renowned knight might you not be made knight. For of all knights he may be called the chief of knighthood. All the world says that knighthood is evenly divided between three knights—that is, Lancelot of the Lake, Sir Tristram of Lyonesse, and Sir Lamorak of Wales. There are many other noble knights, but there are none that pass these three. Therefore God speed you well, for if you match the Red Knight, you shall be called the fourth knight of the world."

"Sir," said Beaumains, "I would fain be of good fame and knighthood. I would have you know I come of good men, for my father was a noble man. And if you will keep it secret, and this damsel, I will tell you of what kin I am."

Then they both promised faithfully not to reveal who Beaumains was until he gave them leave.

"Truly, then," said he, "my name is Gareth of Orkney, and King Lot was my father, and my mother is King Arthur's sister; and Sir Gawaine is my brother, and Sir Agravaine, and Sir Gaheris, and I am the youngest of them all. And neither King Arthur nor Sir Gawaine know yet who I am."

The Red Knight of the Red Lawns

Now the lady who was besieged in Castle Perilous heard that her sister Linet was approaching with a noble knight to rescue her. So she bade the dwarf who brought the tidings go to a hermitage near, and to take with him wine in two silver flagons, loaves of bread, fat venison, and dainty fowls.

"And a cup of gold I deliver that is rich and precious,' she said, "and bear all this to my hermitage, and put it in the hermit's hands. Then go to my sister and greet her well, and commend me unto that gentle knight, and pray him to eat and to drink, and make him strong; and say to him I thank him for his courtesy and goodness for taking on him such labour for me that never did him bounty or courtesy. Also pray him that he be of good heart and good courage, for he shall meet with a full noble knight, but he has no bounty, courtesy, nor gentleness, for he thinks of nothing but murder, and that is the cause I cannot praise him nor love him."

So Beaumains and the damsel went to the hermitage, and there they drank the wine and ate the venison and the baked fowls. And when they had made a good repast the dwarf returned with his vessels to Castle Perilous. On his way there he met the Red Knight of the Red Lawns, who asked him whence he came and where he had been. Then the dwarf told him his lady's sister had come, and that she had brought with her a knight of King Arthur's court.

"Then I account her trouble but lost," said the Red Knight," "for if she had brought with her Sir Lancelot, Sir Tristram, Sir Lamorak, or Sir Gawaine, I should think myself good enough for them all."

"It may well be," said the dwarf, "but this knight has passed all the perilous passages, and has slain the Black Knight and two others, and vanquished the Red Knight and the Blue Knight, Sir Persant of Inde."

"Then he is one of the four I have just said."

"He is none of those, but he is a king's son."

"What is his name ?" said the Red Knight of the Red Lawns.

"That I will not tell you, but Sir Kay out of scorn called him 'Beaumains'."

"I care not whatever knight he be, for I shall soon be quit of him. And if ever I am a match for him he shall have a shameful death, as many others have had."

"That were pity," said the dwarf, "and it is marvel that you should make such shameful war on noble knights."

That night Beaumains and the damsel stayed in the hermitage. On the morrow they took their horses and rode through a fair forest till they came to a plain, where they saw many pavilions and tents, and a splendid castle, and there was much smoke and great noise. And when they came near the besiegers' camp, Beaumains as he rode saw upon great trees how there hung by the neck full goodly armed knights, their shields with their swords tied round their necks, and gilt spurs upon their heels; and thus hung there shamefully nearly forty knights richly armed.

Then Sir Beaumains' face darkened, and he said: "What means this?"

"Do not lose cheer because of this sight, fair sir," said the damsel, "All these knights came hither to this siege to rescue my sister, Dame Liones; and when the Red Knight of the Red Lawns had overcome them he put them to this shameful death without mercy or pity. And in the same way he will serve you unless you quit."

"Now Christ defend me from such a villainous death and disgrace of arms," said Beaumains, "for rather than fare thus I would be slain like a man in plain battle."

"So it were better for you," said Linet. "Trust not there is any courtesy in the Red Knight; all his foes go to death or shameful murder. And that is pity, for he is a full likely man, well made of body, and a lord of great lands and possessions."

"Truly he may well be a good knight," said Beaumains, "but he uses shameful customs, and it is a marvel he endures so long, and that the noble knights of my lord Arthur have not dealt with him."

Then they rode to the dikes, and saw they were double-diked, with full warlike walls, and there were lodged many great knights near the walls, and there was a great noise of minstrelsy.

Fast by was a sycamore tree, and there hung a horn, the greatest that ever they had seen, made out of an elephant's tusk. The Knight of the Red Lawns had hung it there, so that if any errant knight came he must blow that horn, and then the Red Knight would arm himself and come to do battle.

"I pray you, sir, blow not the horn till it be high noon," said the damsel Linet, "for now it is about six o'clock, and at this time his might increases, so that, as men say, he has seven men's strength."

"Ah, fie for shame, fair damsel, never more speak so to me," said Beaumains, "for if he were as good a knight as ever was, I shall never fail him in his greatest might, for either I will win honour honourably, or die knightly in the field."

Therewith Beaumains blew the horn so eagerly that all the camp and the castle rang with it. Then there leaped knights out of their tents and pavilions, and those within the castle looked over the walls, and out of the windows.

Then the Red Knight of the Red Lawns armed himself hastily, and two barons set his spurs upon his heels, and all was blood red, his armour, spear, and shield. And an earl buckled his helmet upon his head, and then they brought him a red spear and a red steed, and so he rode into a little vale under the castle, that all who were in the castle and in the besieging camp might behold the battle.

The Lady of Castle Perilous

"Sir," said the damsel Linet to Sir Beaumains, "look you, be glad and gay, for here is your deadly enemy, and there at yonder window is my lady, my sister, Dame Liones."

"Where?" said Beaumains.

"Yonder," and the damsel pointed with her finger.

"She is the fairest lady that ever I looked on," said Beaumains, "and I ask no better for which to do battle."

And he kept looking up to the window with a glad countenance.

And the Lady Liones made a deep curtsey to him, and they both waved their hands.

With that the Red Knight of the Red Lawns called to Beaumains: "Leave looking, Sir Knight, and behold me, for I warn you well she is my lady, and for her I have done many strong battles."

"If you have so done," said Beaumains, "it seems to me it was but waste labour, for she loves none of your fellowship, and to love one who loves not you is great folly. For if I understood she was not glad of my coming, I should think again before I did battle for her. But I know by the besieging of this castle that she will have nothing to do with you. Therefore, know well, you Red Knight of the Red Lawns, I love her and will rescue her, or else die."

"Say you that?" said the Red Knight. "It seems to me you ought to beware, by reason of yonder knights whom you saw hanging on those trees."

"Fie for shame," said Beaumains, "that ever you should do or say such evil, for in that you shame yourself and knighthood. And now you think that the sight of those hanged knights should frighten me? Nay, truly, not so. That shameful sight causes me to have courage and boldness against you more than I would have had if you were a well-ruled knight."

"Make ready," said the Red Knight of the Red Lawns, "and talk no longer with me."

Then Beaumains bade Linet go to a safe distance, and both knights levelled their spears and rushed together with all their might, so that they hurled each other to the ground, where both lay for a while sorely stunned. All those who were in the castle and the camp thought their necks must be broken, and many said that the strange knight was a big man and a noble jouster, for before then they had never seen any warrior ever match the Red Knight of the Red Lawns.

Then Beaumains and the Red Knight left their horses, and put their shields before them, and ran together like two fierce lions, and each gave the other such blows on the helmets that they both reeled back two strides—then they recovered and dealt such strokes that they hewed great pieces out of their armour and their shields.

Thus they fought till it was past noon, and after resting awhile, the battle went on again till evening, and none who beheld them could tell which was likely to win.

The Red Knight was a wily warrior, and his crafty fighting taught Beaumains to be wise, although he bought his experience dearly. For the Red Knight struck him on the hand, so that his sword fell out of it; and then he gave him yet another blow on the helm, so that Beaumains fell grovelling to the earth, and the Red Knight fell over him, to hold him down.

Then cried the maiden Linet aloud: "Oh, Sir Beaumains, where is your courage? Alas, my lady sister beholds you, and she sobs and weeps, and makes my heart heavy!"

When Sir Beaumains heard this, he started up with great might and leapt to his sword, and gripping it in his hand, he rushed again on the Red Knight, and they fought a new battle together.

But Sir Beaumains doubled his strokes, and striking the knight's sword out of his hand, felled him to the earth. And he unlaced his helmet to slay him, but the Red Knight cried aloud: "O, noble knight, I yield to your mercy!"

"I may not with honour save your life," he said, "because of the shameful deaths you have caused full many good knights to die."

"Sir," said the Red Knight of the Red Lawns, "hold your hand,

and you shall know the cause why I put them to so shameful a death."

"Say on," said Beaumains.

"Sir, I once loved a fair lady, and her brother was slain, and she said it was Sir Lancelot of the Lake, or else Sir Gawaine; and she prayed me that as I loved her heartily I would make her a promise by the faith of my knighthood to labour daily in arms until I met with one of them, and all whom I overcame I should put to a villainous death. This is the cause why I have put all these knights to death, and ensured her vengeance against all King Arthur's knights."

Then came many earls and barons and noble knights, beseeching Beaumains to save the Red Knight's life, and to make him a prisoner. They all fell upon their knees and prayed him to have mercy.

"Fair lords, said Beaumains, "be sure I am full loath to slay this knight, nevertheless he has done great ill and shamefully. But insomuch as all that he did was at a lady's request, I blame him the less, and so for your sake I will release him. He shall have his life upon this covenant—that he go within Castle Perilous and yield there to the Lady Liones, and if she will forgive and acquit him, I will willingly, provided that he make her amends for all the trespass he has done against her and her lands."

"All this will I do as you command," said the Red Knight of the Red Lawns, "and certain assurance and sureties you shall have."

Then the damsel Linet dressed his wounds, and those of Sir Beaumains. Ten days they sojourned in their tents, and the Red Knight made his lords and servants do all the pleasure they could to Sir Beaumains, and he prayed pardon of the Lady Liones for all the wrongs he had done her.

Then Beaumains told Linet he desired to see her sister, his lady.

"I would fain you saw her," she replied.

So Beaumains armed himself, and took his horse and his spear, and rode straight to Castle Perilous.

When he came to the gate he found many men armed, and the drawbridge pulled up, and the port closed. He marvelled why they would not suffer him to enter. Then he looked up to the window, and there he saw the fair Liones.

"Go your way, Sir Beaumains," she cried, "for as yet you shall not have wholly my love, until the time that you are called one of the number of the worthy knights. Therefore go labour honourably for twelve months, and then you shall hear new tidings."

"Alas, fair lady," said Beaumains, "I have not deserved that you should show me this strangeness. I thought I should have had right good cheer with you—I am well sure that I have bought your love with part of the best blood within my body."

"Fair courteous knight, be not displeased," said the Lady Liones. "Your great travail and good love shall not be lost, for I consider your great toil and labour, your bounty and your goodness, as I ought to do. Therefore go your way, and be of good comfort, for all shall be for your glory and for the best. A twelvemonth will soon be done, and trust me, fair knight, I shall be true to you, and never forsake you, but to my death I shall love you, and none other."

Thus the noble knight, Sir Gareth, a king's son—whom Kay had mocked as his "Kitchen Knight"—won for himself deathless honour and his peerless bride. And he and Dame Liones, the Lady of the Castle Perilous, plighted troth to love each other, and never to fail while their life lasted.

THE FOREST KNIGHT

The Boyhood of Tristram

There was once a king called Meliodas, and he was lord of the country of Lyonesse, and this King Meliodas was as noble a knight as any living at that time. His wife was sister of King Mark of Cornwall. She was called Elizabeth, and she was both good and fair. At that time King Arthur was king over the whole of England, Wales, and Scotland, and of many other realms. There were many princes of different countries, but they all held their lands from King Arthur. For in Wales were two kings, and in the north many kings; and in Cornwall and in the west were two kings; also in Ireland there were two or three; and all were under the obeisance of King Arthur.

The wife of King Meliodas was a gentle lady, and well she loved her husband, and he her, and they were very happy together. But in that country lived a lady who was very angry because long ago she had wanted to marry King Meliodas herself, although he had never cared for her. One day when the king rode out hunting, she made him by enchantment chase a hart by himself, till he came to an old castle, and there he was at once taken prisoner by the wicked lady.

When the Queen Elizabeth missed her husband, she was nearly out of her mind with grief, and taking a gentlewoman with her, she ran out into the forest to seek the king.

And there in the middle of the cold and lonely forest, a little son was born, but death came to the poor mother. And when the queen saw that there was no help but that she must die and depart out of this world, then she was very sad.

"When you see my lord, King Meliodas, commend me to him," she said to her gentlewoman, "and tell him what I have endured here for his love, and how I must die here for his sake, with none to help me. And let him know that I am full sorry to depart out of this world from him, therefore pray him not to forget me. Now let me see my little child, for whom I have had all this sorrow." And when she saw him, she said in tender jesting, "Ah, my little son, you have killed your mother, and therefore I suppose that you who are a mur-

69

derer so young, are full likely to be a manly man in your age." Then she charged the gentlewoman that she should beseech King Meliodas to call the child "Tristram"—that is as much as to say, "born in sorrow".

And with that, this queen died.

In the meanwhile, Merlin the magician delivered King Meliodas out of prison on the morning after the death of his queen, and when the king came home, the sorrow that he made for his queen no tongue could tell.

For seven years King Meliodas mourned for his wife, and all this time the young Tristram was nourished well.

But then it happened that King Meliodas wedded Duke Howell's daughter, of Brittany. By and by the new queen had children of her own, and she grew jealous and angry that her children should not enjoy the country of Lyonesse, and because of this she planned to kill young Tristram. So she put some poison into a silver cup, in the chamber where Tristram and her children played together, intending that when Tristram was thirsty he should drink it. But it happened that the queen's own little son as he was in the chamber saw the cup, and being thirsty and thinking it was good to drink, he swallowed it eagerly, and thereupon suddenly died.

When the queen knew of her son's death, you may well imagine how grieved she was. But the king as yet understood nothing of her treason. Notwithstanding the death of her child, however, the queen would not give up her wicked intention, but again she got some more poison and put it into a cup.

By chance King Meliodas found the wine in which the poison was, and being very thirsty, he took the cup to drink of it. Just as he was going to drink the queen saw him, and running to him she pulled the cup suddenly away.

The king marvelled why she did so, and remembered how her son was suddenly slain with poison. Then he took her by the hand and said: "You false traitress, you shall tell me what manner of drink this is, or else I will slay you."

"Ah, mercy, my lord," she cried, "and I will tell you all."

Then she told him how she would have slain Tristram so that her own children should inherit the land.

"Well," said King Meliodas, "for this you shall be tried by law."

By assent of the barons the wicked queen was condemned to be burnt, and a great fire was made. But just as she was at the fire to undergo her sentence, young Tristram knelt before King Meliodas and beseeched him to grant him a boon.

"I will, gladly," said the king.

"Then," said young Tristram, "give me the life of your queen, my stepmother."

"That is not rightfully asked, for you ought of right to hate her, because she would have slain you, and for your sake there is most reason she should die."

"Sir," said Tristram, "as for that, I beseech you of your mercy that you will forgive her; and as for my part, God forgive her, as I do! And since it pleased your Highness to grant me my boon, for God's love I require you to keep your promise."

"Since that is so, I will let you have her life," said the king. "I give her to you. Go to the fire and take her, and do with her what you will."

So Tristram went to the fire, and by commandment of the king delivered the queen from death.

For a long time King Meliodas would have nothing more to do with her, but at last by the good influence of young Tristram he was reconciled to his wife. The queen never forgot how good Tristram had been to her, and ever afterwards she loved him dearly.

A Knight Royal

King Meliodas sought out a tutor who was wise and learned, and under his care he sent young Tristram into France to learn the language and customs, and deeds of arms. There with his tutor, Gouvernail, Tristram stayed more than seven years. When he could speak the language well, and had learnt all he could learn in that country, he came home again to his father. So Tristram learnt to be a harper, passing all others—there was not to be found his equal in any country; and afterwards, as he grew in might and strength, he laboured ever in hunting and hawking, more than any gentleman that was ever heard of. He set in order good measures concerning forest lore, and beasts of chase, and all manner of vermin, with all the terms used in hunting and hawking. Therefore the Book of the

Chase, of Hunting and Hawking, is called the Book of Sir Tristram. Wherefore, all gentlemen that bear arms ought of right to honour Sir Tristram, for he taught such terms as gentlemen use to this day.

Tristram remained away till he was big and strong, and nineteen years old. When he returned home King Meliodas had great joy in his son, and so had the queen his wife.

Soon after Tristram's return from France, it happened that King Anguish of Ireland sent to King Mark of Cornwall for his tribute, which Cornwall had paid many winters. But for seven years King Mark had not paid it, and now he and his barons gave answer to the messenger from Ireland that they would pay nothing.

"Tell your lord," they said, "that if he wishes always to have tribute of Cornwall, let him send a trusty knight who will fight for his right, and we shall find another to defend our right."

King Anguish was very angry at this answer, and he sent Sir Marhaus, the good knight, who was of the Round Table, and brother of the queen of Ireland, to Cornwall to do battle for the tribute.

King Mark was very sorry when he heard that the good and noble knight Sir Marhaus had arrived at Tintagel to fight for Ireland, for he knew no knight who dared do battle with him.

Thus Sir Marhaus remained in his ship off the coast, and every day he sent to King Mark to pay the tribute that was owing for seven years, or else to find a knight to fight for him. And the people of Cornwall made a proclamation in every place that whatever knight would fight to save the tribute of Cornwall, he would be rewarded so that he would fare the better for the rest of his life.

When young Tristram heard of this he asked leave of his father to go to King Mark and be made knight by him. King Meliodas willingly agreed, so Tristram rode into Cornwall. And when he came there he went to King Mark and said: "Sir, if you will give me the order of knighthood, I will do battle with Sir Marhaus."

"Who are you?" said the king, "and from where are you come?"

"Sir, I come from King Meliodas, who wedded your sister; and my name is Tristram, and in the country of Lyonesse was I born."

"You say well," said the king, "and if you will do this battle, I will make you knight."

Sir Marhaus heard that the king of Cornwall had found a young knight ready to do battle to the utmost with him. "That is well," he said to the messenger, "but tell King Mark I will fight with no knight unless he be of royal blood, that is to say, either a king's son, or a queen's son, born of a prince or a princess."

King Mark sent for Sir Tristram and told him of Sir Marhaus's message.

"Let him know," said Tristram, "that I am come on father's and mother's side of blood as noble as he is. For, sir, now you shall know that I am King Meliodas's son, born of your own sister, Lady Elizabeth, who died in the forest at my birth."

"Yea!" cried King Mark. "Fair nephew, you are welcome to me."

Then in all haste King Mark ordered that Sir Tristram should be horsed and armed in the best manner that could be had for gold and silver, and he sent word to Sir Marhaus that a better born man than himself was ready to fight with him.

It was agreed that the battle should take place on an island near which lay Sir Marhaus's ship at anchor. So Sir Tristram was put into a vessel, both he and his horse, with everything that was needful for both of them. When Sir Tristram arrived on the island he looked to the further side, and there he saw six ships lying at anchor, and under the shadow of the ships on land appeared the noble knight, Sir Marhaus of Ireland. Then Sir Tristram bade his servant Gouvernail bring his horse to land, and help him to arm, and when he was in his saddle, well apparelled, with his shield ready on his shoulder, he bade Gouvernail go back again to his vessel.

"Commend me to my uncle, King Mark," he said, "and pray him if I be slain in the battle to bury my body as seems best to him, and bid him know I will never yield for cowardice."

When Sir Marhaus saw Sir Tristram, and how young he was, he was sorry for his daring, and he counselled him to return to his vessel; for the best knights in England and in the world had been matched with Sir Marhaus, and he had overthrown them.

But Sir Tristram replied that he could not forsake the quarrel, because for that he had been made knight. He was a king's son, born of a queen, and he had promised his uncle, King Mark, to fight to the utmost and deliver Cornwall from the old tribute.

Sir Marhaus, having heard Tristram say what he would, spoke: "Fair knight, since it is the case that you seek to win worship because of me, I let you know that you will lose none, if you can stand me three strokes; for because of my noble deeds, proved and seen, King Arthur made me Knight of the Round Table."

Then they levelled their spears and met so fiercely together that they struck each other down, horse and all. Sir Marhaus struck Tristram a great wound in the side with his spear, and then leaping clear of their horses, they pulled out their swords, and throwing their shields before them, lashed together as men that were wild and courageous. But when they had fought for a long time, Sir Tristram was fresher and stronger than Sir Marhaus, and with a mighty stroke he struck Sir Marhaus on the head such a blow that it went through his helmet, and through the coif of steel, and through the brain pan, and the sword stuck fast, so that Sir Tristram had to pull thrice at it before he could pull it out. And Sir Marhaus fell down on his knees, the edge of Tristram's sword left in his brain pan. Then suddenly he stumbled to his feet, and throwing his sword and his shield from him, he ran to his ships and fled his way; and Sir Tristram kept ever afterwards his shield and his sword

So Sir Marhaus and his fellowship departed into Ireland. And as soon as he came to King Anguish, he had his wounds searched. And there in his head was found a piece of Sir Tristram's sword, and none of the surgeons was ever able to get it out, so Sir Marhaus died.

But after he was dead the queen of Ireland, his sister, kept that piece of the sword always with her, for she determined to be revenged if ever she could.

La Belle Iseult

Sir Tristram also had been sorely wounded, and after the fight with Sir Marhaus he sank down on a little hill and could scarcely move. Then came Gouvernail with his vessel, and King Mark and his barons came in procession, and when they got back to Cornwall the king took Tristram in his arms, and he and Sir Dinas, the steward, carried Sir Tristram into the Castle of Tintagel. There he was tended in the best manner and laid in bed. And when King Mark saw his wounds he wept heartily, and so did all his lords.

So Sir Tristram lay there a month and more, and ever he was likely to die of that stroke which Sir Marhaus smote him first with the spear. For the head of the spear was poisoned.

King Mark and all his barons were sad, for they thought that Sir

Tristram would not recover from his wound. The king caused all sorts of doctors and surgeons to be sent for, both men and women, and there was not one who would promise that Tristram should live.

Then came a lady, who was a right wise lady, and she said plainly that Tristram would never be whole unless he went into the same country where the poison came from, and in that country he would be helped, or not at all.

When King Mark heard this he ordered a fair vessel, well provisioned, to be got ready for Sir Tristram, and the sick knight was put therein, and Gouvernail with him, and Sir Tristram took his harp with him. So they put out to sea, to sail to Ireland, and by good fortune they arrived in Ireland fast by a castle where the king and queen were, and on their arrival Tristram sat and harped in his bed a merry lay, such a one as they had never any of them heard in Ireland before that time.

When the king and queen were told of the knight who was such a harper, the king immediately sent for him and had his wounds attended to, and then he asked him his name.

"I am of the country of Lyonesse, and my name is Tramtrist, and I was wounded in battle, as I fought for a lady's right," answered Tristram.

"Truly," said King Anguish, "you shall have all the help in this land that you may have. But I let you know that in Cornwall I had a great loss, for there I lost the best knight of the world, his name was Marhaus—a full noble knight, and a Knight of the Round Table," and he told Tristram how Marhaus had been slain.

Sir Tristram made a semblance of being sorry, but he knew better than the king how it was. He was afraid to reveal his real name, so he still pretended it was "Tramtrist".

King Anguish, as a great favour, made Tramtrist to be put into his daughter's keeping because she was a skilful surgeon. She discovered there was poison in the wound, and in course of time she healed him. Then Tristram learned to have a great love for the beautiful Iseult, for she was at that time the fairest maid and lady of the world.

At that time there was a Saracen knight in the country who was much liked by the king and queen. Sir Palamides was attracted to the beautiful Iseult, and he offered her many gifts, for he loved her well. All this Sir Tristram saw, and full well he knew Sir Palamides for a noble knight and a mighty man. And he had a great grudge against Palamides, for Iseult told Tristram that the Saracen was willing to be christened for her sake. Thus there was great envy between Tristram and Sir Palamides.

Then it happened that King Anguish proclaimed a splendid tournament for a lady who was called the "Lady of the Lawns", and she was a near cousin of the king's. Whatever man won her, should wed her after three days and have all her lands.

One day La Belle Iseult came to Sir Tristram, and told him of this tournament.

"Fair lady," he replied, "I am but a feeble knight, and lately I would have been dead if it had not been for your good ladyship. Now, what would you that I should do? You know well that I cannot joust."

"Ah, Tramtrist," said La Belle Iseult, "why will you not take part in that tournament? I know well Sir Palamides will be there to do what he can, and therefore, Tramtrist, I pray you to be there also, or else Sir Palamides is likely to win the prize."

"Madam," said Tristram, "as for that, it may be so, for he is a proved knight, and I am but a young knight and lately made. But if I thought you would be my lady, I would go to that tournament, provided that you will keep my counsel and let no creature know I shall joust, except yourself."

"Do your best," said La Belle Iseult, "and I will provide you with horse and armour."

On the first day of the jousts came Sir Palamides with a black shield, and he overthrew many knights, so that all the people marvelled at him.

On the morrow Sir Palamides made ready to come into the field as he did the first day. And there he struck down the "King with a Hundred Knights" and the king of Scotland.

La Belle Iseult had provided for Sir Tristram a white horse and white armour, and when he was well arrayed, she let him out at a private gate, and so he rode forth into the field, like a bright angel.

Sir Palamides quickly saw him, and he shaped his spear at Tristram, and Tristram again at him, and then Sir Tristram struck down Palamides to the earth.

After that, no one would joust with Tristram, but all who were there kept out of his way.

Sir Palamides was sorely ashamed at receiving a fall, and, as pri-

vate as he could, he withdrew from the field. Sir Tristram saw all
this, and lightly he rode after Sir Palamides, and overtook him and
bade him turn, for he would test him better before he departed. Then
Palamides turned, and both lashed at each other with their swords.
But at the first stroke Sir Tristram struck down Palamides, and gave
him such a stroke upon the head that he fell to the earth. Then
Tristram bade him yield and do his command or else he would slay
him.

When Sir Palamides saw his countenance he dreaded his blows
so much that he granted everything he asked.

Tristram made him promise that he would forsake following La
Belle Iseult, and also for a twelvemonth and a day that he should
bear no arms nor trappings of war.

"Promise me this or here shall you die," said Tristram.

. "Alas," said Palamides, "I am shamed for ever!" But he swore to
do as Tristram had commanded, and in his spite and anger, he cut
off his armour and threw it away.

Tristram then rode to the gate, which La Belle Iseult kept for
him, and there she made him good cheer.

The king and queen soon discovered that it was Tramtrist who
struck down Palamides, and then he was made much more of than
before.

The Broken Sword

Thus for a long time Sir Tristram stayed on in Ireland, and he was
well cherished by the king and the queen and La Belle Iseult. But
one day when he was out the queen and Iseult went into his room,
and there, as it lay on the bed, the queen beheld his sword. The
queen drew the sword from the scabbard and looked at it, and both
she and La Belle Iseult thought it a fair sword. But within a foot and
a half from the point there was a great piece broken out of the edge.

When the queen saw that gap in the sword, she remembered the
piece of a sword that had been found in the brain pan of Sir Marhaus,
her brother.

"Alas!" she cried to her daughter, "this is the same traitor knight
who slew my brother, your uncle."

Iseult was sorely sad to hear this, for she loved Sir Tristram well.

The queen went at once to her own chamber, and taking out from her coffer the piece of sword that had been found in Sir Marhaus's head, she ran with it to the sword that lay on the bed. And when she put the missing piece against the blade, it was just as it might be when it was new broken.

The queen was so angry at this discovery that she gripped the sword fiercely in her hand and ran with all her might against Tristram where he sat unarmed.

She would have thrust him through, then and there, had not his squire, Sir Hebes, caught her in his arms and pulled the sword from her. She ran to King Anguish, her husband.

"Oh, my lord," she cried, falling on her knees before him, "here have you in your house that traitor knight who slew my brother and your servant, the noble knight, Sir Marhaus."

"Who is that? And where is he?" said the king.

"Sir," she said, "it is Sir Tramtrist, the same knight whom my daughter healed."

"Alas," said the king, "I am much grieved for that, for he is as full noble a knight as ever I saw in field. But I charge you, have no more to do with him but let me deal with him."

Then the king went into the chamber to Sir Tramtrist, where he found him all ready armed to mount upon his horse.

"Nay, Tramtrist," said the king, "it will not avail you to defy me. But this much I will do for my honour and your love. Inasmuch as you are within my court it were no honour for me to slay you. Therefore, I will give you leave to depart, on condition that you will tell me who was your father, and what is your name, and if you slew Sir Marhaus, the queen's brother."

Then Tristram told King Anguish the whole story, and at the end the king said: "Truly, I may not say but you did as a knight should, and it was your part to do your best for your quarrel, and to increase your renown as a knight should. But I cannot keep you in this country in accordance with my honour."

"Sir," said Tristram, "I thank you for the great kindness I have had here, and for the great goodness my lady your daughter has shown me. You may win more by my life than by my death, for in parts of England perhaps I may do you service at some season, so that you will be glad you ever showed me honour. Moreover, I promise you, as I am true knight, that in all places I shall be my lady your daughter's servant and knight, in right and in wrong, and I shall never fail her. Also, I beseech your good grace that I may take my leave of your daughter, and of all the barons and knights."

"Willingly," said King Anguish.

Then Sir Tristram went to La Belle Iseult and took his leave of her.

"Oh, gentle knight," said Iseult, "full sad am I at your departing, for I never saw man to whom I felt such good will." And she wept heartily.

"Madam," said Sir Tristram, "now you shall know that my name is Tristram of Lyonesse, son of King Meliodas, and of his queen. And I promise you faithfully that I will be your knight all the days of my life."

"Great thanks!" said La Belle Iseult. "And I promise you that for the next seven years I will never marry but with your assent, and whom you will that I shall marry, him will I have, if he will have me."

Then Sir Tristram gave her a ring, and she gave him another, and so he departed from her, leaving her in great sorrow.

How Sir Tristram came to Camelot

Thus Sir Tristram departed from Ireland and sailed across the sea, and with a good wind he arrived at Tintagel in Cornwall. After spending some time at home, Tristram, by leave of his father, returned to the court of King Mark of Cornwall, where he lived in great joy for a long time, until at last there fell a great jealousy and unkindness between King Mark and himself, for they both loved the same lady.

One day Tristram was suddenly attacked by three knights, and although he overcame them all and wounded them sorely, yet he was badly hurt himself in the conflict.

King Mark was one of these assailants, but he would not let it be known, and as for Sir Tristram he did not know it was the king with whom he had been fighting. The attendants of the king came to console Tristram as he lay sick in bed, for the crafty king pretended to be sorry for his nephew. Thus passed many days and weeks, and apparently all was forgiven and forgotten.

But as long as King Mark lived he never afterwards loved Sir

Tristram. Though there was fair speech, love there was none. The king cast always in his heart how he might destroy his nephew. Then it inwardly occurred to him to send Sir Tristram into Ireland to fetch La Belle Iseult. For Sir Tristram had so often praised her beauty and her goodness that King Mark said he would wed her, wherefore he begged Sir Tristram to take his way into Ireland on an embassy. And all this was done with the intention of slaying Sir Tristram, for Mark knew of the enmity of King Anguish.

Nevertheless, since it was his uncle's pleasure, Sir Tristram would not refuse the errand because of any peril that might befall himself, but he made ready to go in the goodliest fashion that could be devised, taking with him the noblest knights he could find at court.

So Sir Tristram departed and put to sea with all his company. But as soon as they were out on the broad sea, a tempest took them and drove them back to the coast of England, where they arrived fast by Camelot; and very glad they were to get safe to shore. When they were landed, Sir Tristram set up his pavilion on the lands of Camelot, and had his shield hung on the pavilion.

Now just at that time two knights, who were brothers, Sir Bleoberis and Sir Blamor de Ganis, nephews of Sir Lancelot of the Lake, summoned King Anguish of Ireland to come to court, on pain of forfeiture of King Arthur's good grace. And if the king of Ireland came not at the day assigned and set, he should lose his lands.

It happened that on the appointed day neither King Arthur nor Sir Lancelot could be there to give the judgment, for King Arthur was with Sir Lancelot at his Castle of Joyous Gard. King Arthur, therefore, assigned King Carados and the king of Scots to be at Camelot that day as judges, and while they were there, King Anguish of Ireland came to know his accusers.

Then Blamor de Ganis accused the king of Ireland of treason, that he had slain a cousin of the English knight's in his court in Ireland, by treachery.

King Anguish was sorely abashed at this accusation. He had come at the summons of King Arthur, and before he reached Camelot he did not even know why he had been sent for. When he heard what Sir Blamor had to say, he understood full well there was no other remedy but to answer him knightly. For in those days it was the custom, if any man were accused of treason and murder, that he should fight body for body, or else find another knight to fight for him. All kinds of murder in those days were called "treason". The judges granted him a respite of three days to give his answer.

In the meantime, while Sir Tristram was in his pavilion at Camelot, Gouvernail, his man, came and told him how King Anguish of Ireland had come thither, and how he was put in great distress, and how he had been summoned and accused of murder.

"Truly," said Sir Tristram, "those are the best tidings that have come to me these seven years, for now shall the king of Ireland have need of my help, for I dare say there is no knight in this country, not of Arthur's court, that dares to do battle with Sir Blamor de Ganis. To win the love of the king of Ireland, I will take the battle upon me, and therefore."

So Gouvernail went to King Anguish of Ireland to tell him that Sir Tristram of Lyonesse, for the good grace he was shown in the king's lands, would now reward him.

So King Anguish came to Sir Tristram's pavilion.

When Sir Tristram saw the king, he ran towards him and would have held his stirrup. But the king leapt from his horse lightly, and they both embraced each other.

"My gracious lord," said Sir Tristram, "great thanks for all your goodness shown me in your country. At that time I promised to do you service if ever it lay in my power."

"Gentle Knight," said the king, "now have I great need of knight's help. I am summoned from my country, and accused, because of the death of a knight who was kin to the good knight Sir Lancelot, wherefore Sir Blamor de Ganis, brother of Sir Bleoberis, has challenged me to fight with him, or else to find a knight in my stead. I know well that those who come of King Ban's race, as Sir Lancelot and those others, are very good knights, and as hard men to conquer in battle as any that I know now living."

"Sir," said Sir Tristram, "because of the honour you showed me in Ireland, and for my lady your daughter's sake, La Belle Iseult, I will take the battle for you, on condition that you shall grant me two things. One is that you shall swear to me that you are in the right, and that you never consented to the knight's death. Afterwards, when I have done this battle, if God give me grace that I succeed, you shall give me a reward, what thing reasonable that I will ask of you."

"Truly," said the king, "you shall have whatever you shall ask."

"Rather Death than Dishonour"

"Now make your answer that your champion is ready," said Sir Tristram to King Anguish, "for I shall die in your quarrel rather than be a coward."

"I have no doubt of you," said the king, "even if you had to do battle with Sir Lancelot of the Lake."

"Sir," said Tristram, "as for Sir Lancelot, he is called the noblest knight of the world, and know you well that the knights of his blood are noble men and fear shame; as for Sir Bleoberis, brother to Sir Blamor, I have done battle with him, therefore, on my head, it is no shame to call him a good knight."

"It is reported," said King Anguish, "that Sir Blamor is the hardier knight."

"Sir, as for that, let him be, he shall never be refused, were he the best knight that now bears shield or spear."

King Anguish departed to King Carados and the kings who were that time judges, and told them he had found his champion ready. Then, by command of the kings, Sir Tristram and Sir Blamor de Ganis were sent for to hear the charge.

When they came before the judges, many kings and knights beheld Sir Tristram, and there was much talking about him, because he had slain Sir Marhaus, the good knight, and because he overthrew in jousting the noble Saracen, Sir Palamides.

Having received their charge, the champions withdrew to make ready for battle.

Then said Sir Bleoberis to his brother, Sir Blamor: "Dear brother, remember of what kin we are come, and what a man is Sir Lancelot of the Lake, neither further nor nearer than brother's children. There was never any of our kin that was shamed in battle—but would rather suffer death, than to be shamed!"

"Brother," said Blamor, "have no doubt of me, for I shall never shame any of my blood. He shall slay me rather than I shall yield."

Then he took his horse at one end of the lists, and Sir Tristram at the other end, and so they levelled their spears and came together as though it were thunder, and there Sir Tristram, through great might, struck down Sir Blamor and his horse to the earth.

Sir Blamor leapt quickly clear of his horse, and pulling out his sword, threw his shield before him and bade Sir Tristram alight.

Sir Tristram alighted, and there they lashed together strongly, striking many heavy strokes, so that the kings and knights marvelled greatly; for they fought as if they were mad, never knights were seen to fight more fiercely than they did. Sir Blamor was so hasty he would have no rest, and all men wondered that they had breath to stand on their feet. At the last, Sir Tristram struck Sir Blamor such a blow upon the helmet that he fell down on his side, and Sir Tristram stood and looked at him.

When Sir Blamor could speak, he said thus: "Sir Tristram of Lyonesse, I require you as you are a noble knight, and the best knight that ever I found, that you will slay me outright, for I would rather die with honour than live with shame. You must needs slay me, Sir Tristram, or else you will never win the field, for I will never say the hateful word."

When Sir Tristram heard him speak so knightly, he knew not what to do with him. He thought of both sides—of what blood Sir Blamor came, and how for Sir Lancelot's sake he would be full loath to slay him; yet, on the other side, he could not choose but make Sir Blamor own himself vanquished, or else slay him.

For this was the law of the tournament.

Going to the kings who were judges, Tristram knelt down before them and sought them for their honour, and for King Arthur's and Sir Lancelot's sake, that they would take this matter into their hands.

"For, my fair lords," said Sir Tristram, "it were shame and pity that this noble knight who lies yonder should be slain, for you hear well that shamed he will not be, and I pray to God that he be not shamed nor slain for me. And as for the king for whom I fight, I shall require him, as I am his true champion and true knight in this field, that he will have mercy on this good knight."

"Truly," said King Anguish to Sir Tristram, "I will for your sake be ruled as you will have me, for I know you for my true knight. And therefore I will heartily pray the kings who are here as judges to take the matter into their hands."

Then the kings called Sir Bleoberis to them and asked his advice.

"My lords," said Bleoberis, "though my brother be beaten and has the worse through might of arms, I dare affirm that though Sir Tristram has beaten his body, he has not beaten his heart; and I thank God he is not shamed this day. And rather than he should be shamed, I require you let Sir Tristram slay him outright."

"It shall not be so," said the kings, "for the adversary side, both the king of Ireland and his champion, have pity of Sir Blamor's knighthood."

"My lords," said Bleoberis, "whatever you will, I agree to."

Then the kings called the king of Ireland, and found him good and tractable. By the advice of all of them, Sir Tristram and Sir Bleoberis took up Sir Blamor, and the two brethren were reconciled with King Anguish, and kissed and made friends for ever.

Sir Blamor and Sir Tristram also kissed together, and there they made their oaths that they would never, either of the two brethren, fight with Sir Tristram, and Sir Tristram swore a like oath that he would never fight with them.

And because of that gentle battle all the kindred of Sir Lancelot loved Sir Tristram for ever.

Then King Anguish and Sir Tristram took their leave and sailed into Ireland with great nobleness and joy. When they reached Ireland the king caused it to be made known throughout all the land how and in what manner Sir Tristram had done for him, and the queen, and all who were there made the most of him that they could.

The Magic Draught

Then one day King Anguish asked Sir Tristram why he did not ask his boon, for whatever he had promised him, he should have it without fail.

"Sir," said Tristram, "now is it time, this is all that I desire, that you will give me La Belle Iseult, your daughter, not for myself but for my uncle, Mark, that shall have her to wife, for so have I promised him."

"Alas," said the king, "I had rather than all the land I have that you would wed her yourself."

"Sir, if I did, then were I shamed for ever in this world, and false of my promise. Therefore," said Sir Tristram, "I pray you keep your promise that you gave me. For this is my desire—that you will give me La Belle Iseult to go with me into Cornwall, to be wedded to King Mark, my uncle."

"As for that," said King Anguish, "you shall have her with you to do what it please you."

So La Belle Iseult was made ready to go with Sir Tristram, and Dame Bragwaine went with her for her chief gentlewoman.

Before they left, the queen, Iseult's mother, gave to Dame Bragwaine and to Gouvernail, Sir Tristram's attendant, a magic draught and charged them that whatever day King Mark should wed, on that same day they should give him that draught, so that King Mark should drink to La Belle Iseult.

"And then," said the queen, "I undertake that each shall love the other all the days of their life."

So the drink was given to Dame Bragwaine and to Gouvernail, and directly afterwards Sir Tristram put to sea with La Belle Iseult.

While they were in their cabin it so happened they were thirsty, and they saw a little flask of gold by them, and it seemed by the colour and the taste that it was noble wine. Sir Tristram took the flask in his hand, saying: "Madame Iseult, here is the best drink that ever you drank, which Dame Bragwaine, your maiden, and Gouvernail, my servant, have kept for themselves."

Then they laughed and made good cheer, and each drank to the other in innocent mirth; and they thought that never drink that ever they drank was so sweet nor so good.

But after they had drunk that magic draught they each loved the other so well that never henceforth their love departed.

And this was how first happened the love between Sir Tristram and La Belle Iseult, the which love never departed all the days of their life.

The Quarrel of King and Knight

Sir Tristram and La Belle Iseult put to sea and came to Cornwall, where all the barons met them. And King Mark and Iseult were richly wedded with great splendour.

But because of the magic draught which they had drunk, Sir Tristram and La Belle Iseult ever loved each other dearly, and all the days of his life Sir Tristram was the true and faithful knight of Queen Iseult and ever ready to do her loyal service.

At King Mark's court was a near cousin of Sir Tristram's, called

Sir Andred, a spiteful and malicious man. He envied and hated Sir Tristram, because the latter was so gallant and noble a knight that everyone loved him. Sir Andred dared not quarrel with him openly, but he lay always in watch to find him out in some secret fault so that he might slander him to his uncle. King Mark was only too eager to believe any evil of Tristram, for he had never forgotten the old grudge he bore him.

So it happened one day that Sir Tristram talked with Queen Iseult, and Sir Andred saw them and, hoping to make mischief, went and told the king. King Mark came in a great rage, with his sword in his hand, and called him "false traitor", and would have struck him. But Tristram, being very near, ran under the sword and seized it from the King's hand.

"Where are my knights and my men?" cried the king. I charge you, slay this traitor!"

But not one of them would move.

Sir Tristram, seeing that not one would be against him, made as though he would strike the king, whereupon Mark fled. Then Tristram went his way and armed himself, and taking his horse and his man, rode into the forest.

King Mark sent many knights after him, but Sir Tristram killed two and wounded many more, and not one of them could overcome him. Then King Mark called his council, and asked advice of his barons.

"Sire," said the barons, "we counsel you to send for Sir Tristram, for we would have you know that many men will side him if he is hard pressed. He is called peerless and matchless of any Christian knight, and of his might and hardihood we know none so good a knight, unless it be Sir Lancelot of the Lake. If he depart from your court, and go to King Arthur's court, mark you well, he will find such friends there that he will care nothing for your malice. Therefore, sir, we counsel you to take him into your favour."

"I am willing that he be sent for, that we may be friends," said the king.

Then the barons sent for Sir Tristram, under a safe conduct. When the knight came back to court he was made welcome. Nothing was said about what had happened, and there was sport and amusement. The king and the queen went out hunting, and Tristram went with them.

Iseult of Brittany

Sir Andred, in the meanwhile, was always on the watch to see how he could trap Sir Tristram, and at last his opportunity came. One day, with twelve knights, he fell on him secretly and suddenly, and bound him hand and foot. Then, by assent of King Mark, Tristram was taken to a little chapel on the sea rocks, there to receive judgment, and he was led bound between forty knights.

When he saw there was no escape, but that he must needs die, then he said: "Fair lords, remember what I have done for the country of Cornwall, and what jeopardy I have been in for you. For at the time I fought for the tribute of Cornwall against Sir Marhaus, when you all refused to take the battle, I was promised to be better rewarded. Therefore as you be good, gentle knights, see me not thus shamefully die, for it is a shame to all knighthood thus to treat me. For I dare say that I never yet met with any knight, but I was as good as he, or better."

"Fie upon you," said Sir Andred, "false traitor as you are with your vaunting! For all your boast you shall die this day."

"O Andred, Andred," said Sir Tristram, "you, my kinsman, are to me full unfriendly! But if there were no more but you and I, you would not put me to death."

"No!" said Sir Andred, and therewith he drew his sword and would have slain him.

When Sir Tristram saw this threatening movement, he looked at both his hands, which were fast bound to two knights, and suddenly he pulled them to him, and wrenched them free; then he leaped to his cousin Andred, and wrested his sword out of his hand and struck him to the earth; and thus he fought until he had killed ten knights. Then he got inside the chapel, and held it bravely.

But the outcry was great, and numbers of people—more than a hundred—flocked quickly to Sir Andred. When Sir Tristram saw the people draw near, he remembered he was without armour, and making fast the door of the chapel, he broke the bars of a window, and so leaped out and fell upon the crags into the sea. And at that time neither Sir Andred nor any of his fellows could get at him.

In the meanwhile, Gouvernail and two of Sir Tristram's men

sought their master. When they heard he had escaped, they were very glad, and on the rocks they found him and pulled him up.

Tristram asked where La Belle Iseult was, for he thought Sir Andred's people had carried her away. But Gouvernail replied that she had been shut up in a horrible little hut, kept apart for the use of sick folk, ill of dangerous diseases.

"Alas!" said Sir Tristram, "that is a foul place for such a fair lady, and if I may, she shall not be long there," and so he went with his men and fetched away Queen Iseult, and brought her into a forest to a fair manor, where she remained, for she was afraid to go back to her husband, King Mark.

One day Sir Tristram went into the forest for a little sport, and it so happened that there he fell asleep. And a certain man, whose brother Tristram had killed some time before, came that way, and finding him asleep, shot him through the shoulder with an arrow.

Meanwhile King Mark had been told how Sir Tristram had taken Queen Iseult out of the hut and placed her in the manor, and as soon as the king heard of it, he came thither with many knights to slay Sir Tristram. But he arrived when Tristram was absent in the forest, so he took La Belle Iseult home with him, and afterwards kept her so closely shut up that by no means in her power could she send word to Tristram, nor he to her.

When Sir Tristram returned from the forest to the old manor he found the track of many horses, and thereby he knew his lady was gone. Then he was very sorrowful, and for a long time he endured great pain, for the arrow with which he had been hurt was poisoned.

At last, through some lady who was a cousin to Dame Bragwaine, Queen Iseult sent a message to Sir Tristram. She told him he would by no means be cured in Cornwall, for she was not able to help him. Therefore she bade him haste into Brittany, to King Howell, and there he would find the king's daughter, Iseult of the White Hands, and she would help him

So Sir Tristram and Gouvernail took ship, and sailed to Brittany. King Howell was very glad when he knew it was Sir Tristram of Lyonesse who had come. Tristram said he had come to his country to have help from his daughter, for it had been told him that no one else could cure him.

And there, in a little while, Iseult of Brittany healed Sir Tristram of his hurt.

A great liking grew up between Tristram and Iseult, for that lady was both good and fair, and a woman of noble blood and fame. And because Sir Tristram had such cheer and riches, and all other pleasantness, he almost for a time forgot La Belle Iseult who loved him.

So he agreed to wed Iseult of Brittany, and at last they were wedded, and the marriage was held with great solemnity and splendour.

The Forest of Strange Adventures

When Queen Iseult heard that Sir Tristram was wedded to Iseult of Brittany, she sent him letters by Bragwaine, saying that if it pleased Sir Tristram to go to her court and take with him Iseult of the White Hands, they should be treated right well.

Sir Tristram did not think it well to take his wife to Cornwall, for he knew not what might happen, through the enmity of King Mark. But he called his brother-in-law, Sir Kehydius, and asked him whether he would go with him. He answered that he was ready at all times. So a little vessel was quietly prepared, and therein they went—Sir Tristram, Kehydius, Dame Bragwaine, and Gouvernail.

When they were at sea a contrary wind took them on to the coast of North Wales, near Castle Perilous. Then Tristram said to Bragwaine, "Wait here for me ten days, and Gouvernail, my squire, shall stay with you. And if I come not by the end of that time, take the nearest way into Cornwall, for in this forest are many strange adventures, I have heard say, and some of them I intend to prove before I depart. And when I can, I will come after you."

Sir Tristram and Sir Kehydius took their horses, and left their companions and rode through the forest a mile and more. And there they came across a knight errant, with whom they jousted, but at the first encounter Sir Kehydius got a fall and was sorely wounded. So Sir Tristram and the other knight, Sir Lamorak of Wales, set him on a shield and bore him between them to the lodge of a forester, to whom they gave charge that Sir Kehydius was to be well kept. After three days the other two knights took their horses, and at the crossroads they parted.

As Sir Tristram rode on his way alone, he chanced to meet Sir Kay, the steward. Sir Kay asked Sir Tristram of what country he was. The latter answered that he was of the country of Cornwall.

"It may well be," said Sir Kay sneeringly, "for I never yet heard that ever good knight came out of Cornwall."

"That is evil spoken," said Sir Tristram, "but I require you to tell me your name."

"Sir, my name is Sir Kay, the steward."

"Is that your name?" said Sir Tristram; "now know you well that you are called the shamefullest knight of your tongue now living; howbeit, you are called a good knight, but unfortunate, and most spiteful with your tongue."

Thus they rode together till they came to a bridge, and here stood a knight who would not let them pass till one of them jousted with him. So the knight jousted with Sir Kay, and there he gave him a fall. The knight's name was Sir Tor, half-brother to Sir Lamorak, and they were the sons of Pellinore, with whom King Arthur had once fought.

Then Sir Tristram and Sir Kay rode to their lodging, where they found another knight, named Sir Brandiles, and Sir Tor came thither soon after.

As the four knights sat at supper, three of them spoke all shame of Cornish knights. Tristram heard what they said, and he spoke but little, but he thought the more, and he did not at that time reveal his name.

On the morrow he took his horse and went with them. On the way Sir Brandiles offered to joust with him, and Sir Tristram struck him down, horse and all, to the earth. Then Sir Tor encountered with Sir Tristram, and Sir Tristram struck him also down. Then he rode on alone. Sir Kay followed him, but Tristram would not have his company.

"I would fain know what is that knight's name," said Sir Brandiles, coming up to Sir Kay.

"Come on with me," said Sir Kay, "and we will pray him to tell us his name."

They rode together till they came near Tristram, and saw where he sat by a well and had put off his helmet to drink at the well. When he saw them come, he laced on his helmet, and took his horse and offered to joust.

"Nay," said Sir Brandiles, "we jousted late enough with you, we come not with that intent. But we come to require you of knighthood to tell us your name."

"My fair knights, since that is your desire, and to please you, you shall know that my name is Tristram of Lyonesse, nephew to King Mark of Cornwall."

"In good time, and you are well found!" said Sir Brandiles. "Know you well that we are right glad we have found you, and we are of a fellowship that would be right glad of your company. For you are the knight in the world whom the fellowship of the Round Table most desires."

"I thank them for their great goodness," said Sir Tristram, "but as yet I feel I am unable to be of their fellowship. For I was never of such deeds of worthiness to be in the company of such a fellowship."

"Ah," said Sir Kay, "if you are Sir Tristram of Lyonesse, you are the man now called most of prowess, except Sir Lancelot of the Lake. For that man is not alive, either Christian or heathen, who can find such another knight, to speak of his prowess, and his hands, and his truth withal. For never yet could any one say of him dishonour, and make it good."

Thus they talked a great while, and then they departed one from another, such ways as seemed best to them.

Now about this time a wicked enchantress called the Lady Anna, by fair words and artful cunning enticed King Arthur to ride with her into the Forest Perilous. She was a great sorceress and had loved King Arthur many days, and therefore she came into that country. When King Arthur had gone with her, and his knights missed him, many of them followed after him, such as Sir Lancelot, Brandiles, and others.

The sorceress took King Arthur to her tower, and hoped to win his love, but the king remembered his own lady, Queen Guinevere, and would not love the enchantress for any craft she could do. Then every day she made him ride into the forest with his own knights, with the intent of having him slain. For when this Lady Anna could not have her will she laboured by false means to have King Arthur destroyed and slain.

But the Lady of the Lake—whose name was Nimue—who was always friendly to King Arthur, discovered by her subtle craft that the king was in great danger, and therefore she came into the Forest Perilous to seek after Sir Lancelot or Sir Tristram to help King Arthur. For on that same day the Lady of the Lake knew well King Arthur would be slain unless she had help of one of these two knights.

Thus she rode up and down until she met with Sir Tristram, and as soon as she saw him, she knew him.

"Oh, my lord Sir Tristram," she said, "well are you met, and blessed be the time I have met with you! For this same day and within these two hours shall be done the foulest deed that ever was done in this land."

"Oh, fair damsel," said Sir Tristram, "may I amend it?"

"Come with me," she said, "and with all the haste you may, for you shall see the most worshipful knight of the world hard bested."

Then said Sir Tristram, "I am ready to help such a noble man."

"He is neither better nor worse than the noble King Arthur himself," said the Lady of the Lake.

"God forbid that ever he should be in such distress," said Sir Tristram.

They rode together a great pace until they came to a little castle, and underneath that castle they saw a knight standing on foot, fighting with two knights. Sir Tristram watched them, and at last saw the two knights strike down the one knight, and one of them unlaced his helmet to slay him. And the Lady Anna got King Arthur's sword in her hand to strike off his head.

Then Sir Tristram rushed forward with all his might, crying, "Traitress, traitress, leave that!" and he quickly struck one knight after the other so that both fell dead.

In the meanwhile the Lady of the Lake cried to King Arthur, "Let not that false lady escape!" and King Arthur overtook the wicked sorceress, and with the same sword she held in her hand he struck off her head.

Sir Tristram set King Arthur on horseback and rode forth with him, but he charged the Lady of the Lake not to reveal his name at that time. When the king was mounted, he thanked Sir Tristram heartily and desired to know his name, but Tristram would not tell him, except that he was a poor knight adventurous. And so he bore the king company until he met with some of his own knights.

Within a mile they met with Sir Ector de Maris, who did not know either King Arthur or Sir Tristram, and desired to joust with one of them. Sir Tristram accepted his offer, and at once struck him from his horse. Having done so, he came again to the king, and said: "My lord, yonder is one of your knights, he can bear you fellowship; and another day, by that deed which I have done for you, I trust you will understand that I would do you service."

"Alas," said King Arthur, "let me know whom you are."

"Not at this time," said Sir Tristram.

So he departed, and left King Arthur and Sir Ector together.

The Wild Man of the Woods

On a day appointed, Sir Tristram went back to the forester's lodge where Sir Kehydius had been left to get well of his wounds, and they rode to the ship where Dame Bragwaine and Gouvernail were waiting for them, and so they sailed all together to Cornwall.

Queen Iseult rejoiced more than tongue can tell to see Sir Tristram again, but Tristram could not remain in the Castle of Tintagel, for King Mark still hated him and would have slain him if he could. So taking his horse and armour, he rode away into the forest, and there for many days he dwelt in loneliness and bitter sorrow. No one knew what had become of him. A damsel from the court went out to seek him, but nothing she could say or do would give him any comfort, nor would he eat any meat or drink when she brought it him.

Now came a sad time for poor Sir Tristram. He sorrowed so deeply and was so long in the lonely forest that his mind quite went, and he lost all memory of knightly things. His clothes fell off in tatters, and he waxed lean and poor of flesh; and so he fell into the company of herdsmen and shepherds, and daily they would give him of their meat and drink, and they clipped him with shears, and treated him like a fool.

But although he had lost his mind, he was still brave in spirit and strong in body. Once when his friends the herdsmen were threatened by Sir Dagonet, King Arthur's fool, and two squires, Sir Tristram ran to their help, overthrew Dagonet, killed one of the squires, and drove the other away.

In the meanwhile, his wicked cousin Sir Andred caused it to be noised abroad that Sir Tristram was dead. He got some lady to tell a false tale at King Mark's court, that she was with Sir Tristram when he died, that she had buried him by a well, and that before he died he beseeched King Mark to make his cousin Sir Andred king of the country of Lyonesse, of which Sir Tristram was lord.

King Mark pretended to make great lamentation when he heard that Sir Tristram was dead. But when these tidings reached Queen Iseult she made such sorrow that she was almost out of her mind. She fell ill of grief and lay for a long time sick, nearly at the point of death.

Now in that country there was a giant called Tauleas. From fear of Tristram, for more than seven years he never dared go much at large, but when he heard that Tristram was dead, then he went out daily. So it happened one morning he came across the herdsmen, wandering and lingering round a well in the forest, and sat himself down to rest among them.

While he was there, up came a knight of Cornwall, called Sir Dinant, leading with him a lady. The giant, seeing him, went from the herdsmen and hid himself under a tree; and the knight came to the well, and there he alighted to rest.

As soon as he was away from his horse, the giant Tauleas came between this knight and his horse, and took the horse and leapt on it. Then he rode at Sir Dinant, and seizing him by the collar, pulled him up before him and would have struck off his head.

"Help yonder knight!" cried the herdsmen to Sir Tristram.

Then Tristram saw the sword of the knight where it lay on the ground, and he ran and took it up, and struck off the head of the giant, and so went his way back to the herdsmen again.

Sir Dinant on his return to court told King Mark of the adventure that had befallen him in the forest, and how a wild man had rescued him from the grim giant Tauleas.

"Well," said King Mark, "I will see that wild man."

So within a day or two King Mark commanded his knights and his huntsmen that they should be ready the next morning to hunt, and on the morrow he went into the forest. And when he came to the well he found there, lying asleep, a comely man with a sword by him. The king commanded his knights to take him up gently and bring him to the Castle of Tintagel, which they did. And there they bathed him and washed him, and gave him hot food, so that presently Sir Tristram quite recovered his lost memory.

But all this while there was not a creature who knew Sir Tristram, nor what man he was.

One day the queen, La Belle Iseult, heard of the wild man of the forest and how the king had brought him home to the court. Then Queen Iseult called Dame Bragwaine to her and said, "Come with me, for I will go see this man whom my lord brought from the forest." And they found him in the garden taking his rest, reposing in the sun.

When the queen looked at Sir Tristram, she did not remember him, but as soon as Sir Tristram saw Iseult, he knew her well enough, and he turned away his face and wept.

Now the queen had always a little dog with her that Sir Tristram gave her the first time she ever came into Cornwall, and never would the little dog leave her unless Sir Tristram himself were also near.

As soon as this little dog came near Tristram, she leaped upon him and licked his cheeks and his ears, and whined and jumped about all over him.

"Ah, my lady!" said Dame Bragwaine to La Belle Iseult.

"Alas, alas!" cried the queen, "I see it is mine own lord Sir Tristram!" and she fell down in a swoon, and lay senseless for a long time, for she was startled to see Tristram alive after so long believing him to be dead. By and by, when she could speak, she said, "My lord Sir Tristram, blessed be God you have your life! Now I am sure you will be discovered by means of this little dog, for she will never leave you; and also I am sure that as soon as my lord King Mark knows you, he will banish you out of the country of Cornwall, or else he will destroy you. Therefore grant King Mark his will, and go you to the court of King Arthur, for there you are beloved. And whenever I can, I shall send unto you, and when you like, you can come to see me, and at all times early and late I will be at your command to live as poor a life as ever did queen or lady."

"O madam," cried Sir Tristram, his heart torn with grief and pity, "leave me, I pray, for much anger and danger have I endured for your sake.

Then the queen departed, but the little dog would not leave him.

"For Love of Sir Lancelot!"

Soon after Queen Iseult had departed, came King Mark, and the little dog set upon him and bayed at them all, and by this was discovered Sir Tristram.

"Ah," said King Mark, "I am sorry for your recovery." And he had his barons summoned to judge him to death.

Many of the barons would not consent to that, so by the advice of them all, Sir Tristram was banished out of the country for ten years.

In the meanwhile, arrived a knight of King Arthur's, whose name was Dinadan, and his coming was to seek after Sir Tristram. Then they showed him where Tristram was, armed at all points, ready to start for his ship.

"Now, fair knight," said Dinadan, "before you pass from this court, I challenge you to joust with me."

"With a good will," said Tristram, "if these lords will give me leave."

The barons granted it, and so the knights charged at each other, and there Sir Tristram gave Sir Dinadan a fall. Then Dinadan begged leave to go with him.

"You shall be right welcome," said Sir Tristram. So they took their horses, and rode to the ship together.

When Sir Tristram was on the ship, he turned and spoke to the barons who had gone with him: "Greet well King Mark and all my enemies," he said, "and tell them I will come again when I can."

And forthwith Sir Tristram set out to sea.

At the next landing, near the sea, Sir Tristram and Sir Dinadan met with two knights, Sir Ector de Maris and Sir Bors de Ganis, who challenged them to a trial of strength. Sir Ector jousted with Sir Dinadan and struck him and his horse down, and Sir Tristram would have jousted with Sir Bors, but Sir Bors said he would joust with no Cornish knights, for they are not called men of honour.

Just then up came two more knights, one of whom, Sir Bleoberis, offered to joust with Sir Tristram, who immediately vanquished him with ease.

Then said Sir Bors de Ganis, "I never knew Cornish knight of so great valour, nor so valiant, as that knight who bears the trappings embroidered with crowns."

After this, Sir Tristram and Sir Dinadan left them and rode into a forest, and here a damsel met them, who came for the love of Sir Lancelot to seek after some noble knights of King Arthur's court, to rescue Sir Lancelot. For Queen Morgan le Fay, the wicked sorceress, had resolved by treachery to slay Sir Lancelot, and for that cause she ordained thirty knights to lie in wait for him. This damsel knew of the treachery, and this was the reason she came to seek noble knights to help Sir Lancelot. For that night, or the day after, Sir Lancelot would come where those thirty knights were.

The damsel met first Sir Bors, Sir Bleoberis, Sir Ector, and Sir Driant, and she told them all four of the treason of Morgan le Fay. They promised her that they would be near where Sir Lancelot should meet with the thirty knights. After leaving the four knights, the damsel by chance met Sir Tristram and Sir Dinadan, and these also she told of all the treachery that was ordained for Sir Lancelot.

"Fair damsel," said Sir Tristram, "lead me to the place where they expect to meet with Sir Lancelot."

Soon after, the thirty knights drew near the four knights, and they were all aware of each other. But the thirty knights let the four knights pass, in case they, too, had been ordered to attack Sir Lancelot, and the four knights let the thirty knights pass with the intention of seeing what they could do with Sir Lancelot.

So the thirty knights passed on and came up to Sir Tristram and Sir Dinadan. And as they drew near Sir Tristram cried aloud: "Lo, here is a knight against you, for the love of Sir Lancelot!"

And there he slew two with one spear, and ten with his sword; and then Sir Dinadan rushed into the fray and did well.

So of the thirty knights there went but ten away, and these fled.

Sir Bors de Ganis and his three companions watched this battle, and they saw well it was the same knight who had jousted with them near the sea. Then they took their horses and rode to Sir Tristram, and praised him and thanked him for his good deeds; and they all wanted Sir Tristram to go with them to their lodgings.

But he said nay, he would go to no lodging.

Then all the four knights prayed him to tell them his name.

"Fair lords," said Tristram, "I will not tell you my name at present."

The False Treason of Morgan le Fay

Sir Tristram and Sir Dinadan continued on their way, and as they went they had many adventures. But Dinadan lamented all the while that ever he fell into Sir Tristram's company. For every knight they met wanted to joust with them, and Sir Dinadan liked not so much fighting, and moreover he had many falls.

"You fare as a madman," he said to Sir Tristram, "and I could curse the time that ever I saw you. For in all the world there are not two knights that are so mad as Sir Lancelot and you. For once I fell into the fellowship of Sir Lancelot, as I have now done with you, and he set me such a work that I kept my bed a quarter of a year. Defend me from two such knights, and especially from *your* companionship!"

They found lodging that night with a good man in a priory, where they were well treated. On the morrow Sir Tristram departed, leaving Sir Dinadan in the priory, for the latter was so weary and so sorely bruised that he could not ride. The next day Sir Tristram met with messengers, and they told him there was great proclamation made of a tournament between King Carados of Scotland and the king of North Wales at the Castle of Maidens. These messengers were searching all the country after good knights, and especially King Carados was seeking for Sir Lancelot, and the king of North Wales was seeking for Sir Tristram of Lyonesse.

So Sir Tristram thought he would be at that tournament.

The same day he met with a damsel, who told him he should win great renown from a knight adventurous who did much harm in all that country. When Sir Tristram heard her say so, he was glad to go with her to win honour. They had ridden about six miles when Sir Gawaine met them. He knew the damsel immediately, that she was one of the ladies of the wicked queen, Morgan le Fay.

"Fair knight," said Sir Gawaine, "you shall not ride with that damsel, for she and her lady never did good but ill." Then pulling out his sword, he said, "Damsel, unless you tell me quickly for what cause you lead this knight with you, you shall die for it at once. I know all your lady's treason and yours."

"Mercy, Sir Gawaine!" she cried, "and if you will save my life, I will tell you."

"Say on, and you shall have your life," said Gawaine.

"Sir, Queen Morgan le Fay, my lady, has ordained thirty ladies to seek after Sir Lancelot or Sir Tristram, and these ladies, whoever first meets with either of these two knights, they shall turn them to Morgan le Fay's castle, saying they shall do deeds of worship. And if either of these two knights comes there, there are thirty knights lying and watching in a tower, to wait for Sir Lancelot or Sir Tristram."

Then Sir Gawaine and Sir Tristram agreed to ride to the castle where Morgan le Fay was, and to defy the malice of the thirty knights. And Sir Gawaine kept on thinking that his companion must certainly be Tristram of Lyonesse, for he had heard tell how two knights had slain and beaten thirty knights.

When they came before the castle, Sir Gawaine cried out: "Queen Morgan le Fay, send out your knights whom you have laid to watch for Sir Lancelot and Sir Tristram! Now I know your false treason, and through all places where I ride men shall know of your false treason. And now, you thirty knights, let Sir Gawaine see if you dare come out of your castle!"

Then the queen and all the thirty knights spoke at once, and said: "Sir Gawaine, full well you know what you do and say, for we know you well. But all that you speak and do, you say it from pride of that good knight who is there with you. For there be some of us who know full well the hands of that knight, and know well, Sir Gawaine, it is more for his sake than for yours that we will not come out of this castle."

Finding that Queen Morgan le Fay and her thirty knights were too cowardly to face them openly, Sir Gawaine and Sir Tristram departed from the castle and rode on their travels a day or two together.

They had not gone far before they saw a cruel knight chasing a lady to slay her, for he had already slain her lover. He was called "Sir Breuse Without Pity".

"Hold still," said Sir Gawaine, "and do not show yourself, and you shall see me reward yonder false knight. For if he sees you, he is so well horsed that he will escape away."

Then Sir Gawaine rode between Sir Breuse and the lady, calling out, "False knight, leave her and deal with me!"

Sir Breuse, seeing no one but Sir Gawaine, levelled his spear, and Sir Gawaine did the same, and there Sir Breuse overthrew Sir Gawaine; then as the knight lay on the ground he rode over and across him several times, to destroy him. When Sir Tristram saw him do so villainous a deed, he hurled out against him.

As soon as Sir Breuse saw the shield of Cornwall, he knew well it was Sir Tristram, and away he fled with Sir Tristram after him. Sir Breuse had so good a horse that he got quite away, but Tristram followed him.

After chasing him some way, he saw a fair well, and thither he rode to rest. Alighting from his horse, he tied him to a tree, and pulling off his helmet, he washed his face and hands, and presently he fell asleep.

In the meanwhile came Dame Bragwaine who had sought Sir Tristram many days and many ways in that country. When she came to the well she looked at the sleeping knight and stayed still until he awoke, and then she saluted him, and he her again. She told him how she had sought him far and wide, and how she had letters from Queen Iseult of Cornwall. Tristram read them at once, and very glad he was to have them.

"Lady Bragwaine," he said, "you shall ride with me till that tournament at the Castle of Maidens is over, and then you shall bear letters and tidings back to Queen Iseult."

At the Castle of Maidens

On the first day of the great tournament at the Castle of Maidens Sir Tristram did so gallantly and overthrew so many knights that King Arthur and all the kings and lords who were judges gave him the prize, although they knew him not but named him the "Knight with the Black Shield".

On the morrow, Sir Palamides, who had been fighting for the king of North Wales, left him and rode to King Arthur's side, where was King Carados, and the king of Ireland, and Sir Lancelot's kin, and Sir Gawaine's kin. And the better to disguise themselves, Sir Lancelot and thirty-two knights of his blood had assumed shields of Cornwall. Sir Palamides sent a damsel as messenger to Sir Tristram to ask who he was and what was his name.

"As to that," said Sir Tristram, "tell Sir Palamides he shall not know at this time, nor until I have broken two spears on him. But tell him plainly that side on which he is, I will be on the contrary side."

"Sir," said the damsel, "Sir Palamides will be on King Arthur's side, where the most noble knights of the world be."

"Then," said Sir Tristram, "I will be with the king of North Wales."

When King Arthur came, the trumpets blew for the field, and then began a great fight. King Carados jousted with the king of

North Wales, and there had a fall, whereupon other knights of King Arthur's immediately rushed in and beat back the knights of the king of North Wales. Then Sir Tristram rode in, and began so roughly and so hugely that no one could withstand him, and thus he kept on for a long time. But at the last Tristram fell among the company of King Ban, and was attacked by Sir Bors de Ganis, Sir Ector de Maris, and many other knights. Sir Tristram struck on the right and on the left, so that all lords and ladies spoke of his noble deeds. But in the end he would have had the worse had it not been for the King with the Hundred Knights, who came with his followers and rescued Sir Tristram, and carried him away from those knights who bore the shields of Cornwall.

After this, Sir Tristram saw another troop by themselves, about forty knights together, and Sir Kay was their governor. Sir Tristram rode in amongst them and struck down Sir Kay from his horse, and there he fared among those knights like a greyhound among conies.

Sir Lancelot, meanwhile, found a knight who was sorely wounded on the head; he asked him who had done it.

"Sir," he said, "a knight who bears a black shield. I could curse the time that ever I met with him, for he is a devil and no man."

Sir Lancelot left him, and hoping to meet with Sir Tristram, he rode seeking him, with his sword drawn in his hand. At last he spied him, how he hurled here and there, and at every stroke Sir Tristram well nigh struck down a knight.

"Oh, mercy," said King Arthur, "since the time I bore arms, I never saw knight do such marvellous deeds of valour."

"And if I should attack this knight," said Sir Lancelot to himself, "I should shame myself," and he put up his sword.

The King with a Hundred Knights, and a hundred more men of North Wales, now set upon twenty of Sir Lancelot's kin, and those twenty knights held ever together, and none would fail the other. When Sir Tristram saw the *noblesse* of these twenty knights he marvelled at their good deeds, for he saw by their bearing and conduct that they would rather die than yield the field.

"Now," said Sir Tristram, "well may he be valiant and full of prowess who has such noble knights for his kin, and full like is he to be a noble man who is their leader and governor!" He meant by this, Sir Lancelot of the Lake.

After Sir Tristram had watched them for a long time, he thought it shame to see two hundred knights battering upon twenty knights, so he rode to the king of North Wales, and said: "Sire, leave your fighting with those twenty knights, for you win no renown from them, you are so many and they are so few."

"Now that I see your courage and courtesy," said the king of North Wales, "to please you I will withdraw my knights."

All this while and long before, Sir Lancelot had watched Sir Tristram with the very purpose of having fellowship with him. But suddenly Sir Tristram, Sir Dinadan, and Gouvernail rode their way into the forest so that no man perceived where they went.

Then King Arthur blew for the fighting to cease and gave the king of North Wales the prize, because Sir Tristram was on his side. Sir Lancelot rode here and there like a raging lion because he had lost Sir Tristram, but he had to return without him to King Arthur. Then in all the field there was a noise that with the wind might have been heard two miles off, how the lords and ladies cried: "The Knight with the Black Shield has won the field!"

"Alas," said King Arthur, "what has become of that knight? It is shame to all those in the field so to let him escape away."

Afterwards King Arthur went to his knights and comforted them in the best way he could for having been defeated that day.

"My brave knights," he said, "be not dismayed, even although you have lost the field this day. Be of good cheer, for tomorrow I will be in the field with you and revenge you of your enemies."

The Third Day of the Tournament

Then on the morrow the trumpets blew to the tournament for the third day.

The king of North Wales and the King with the Hundred Knights encountered with King Carados and with the king of Ireland; and there the King with the Hundred Knights struck down King Carados, and the king of North Wales struck down the king of Ireland. Sir Palamides came at once to the help of the fallen knights and made great work, for by his indented shield he was well known. Then King Arthur joined him and did great deeds of arms, and put the king of North Wales and the King of the Hundred Knights to the worse. But Sir Tristram with his black shield came to their help and quickly he jousted with Sir Palamides, and there by fine force he struck Sir Palamides over his horse's croup.

Then cried King Arthur, "Knight with the Black Shield, make ready to me!" and in the same way Sir Tristram struck King Arthur.

By force of Arthur's knights, the king and Sir Palamides were horsed again, and the king with an eager heart, seizing a spear, struck Sir Tristram from one side over his horse. Hotfoot, from the other side, Sir Palamides came upon Sir Tristram, as he was on foot, meaning to override him, but Sir Tristram was aware of him and stooped aside, and with great ire he got him by the arm and pulled him down from his horse

Sir Palamides arose lightly, and they dashed together mightily with their swords, and many kings, queens and lords stood and beheld them. At the last, Sir Tristram struck Sir Palamides upon the helmet three mighty strokes, and at every stroke he gave him, he cried, "Have this for Sir Tristram's sake!" With that, Sir Palamides fell to the earth, grovelling.

Then came the King of the Hundred Knights and brought Sir Tristram a horse, and so he was mounted again. Then he was aware of King Arthur with a naked sword in his hand, and with his spear Sir Tristram ran upon King Arthur. The king boldly awaited him, and with his sword he struck the spear in two. At this Sir Tristram was so astonished that King Arthur gave him three or four great strokes before he could get out his sword, but at last Sir Tristram drew his sword and attacked the other, pressing hard.

Now the great crowd parted them; then Sir Tristram rode here and there, and fought with such fury that eleven of the good knights of the blood of King Ban, who were of Sir Lancelot's kin, were that day struck down by Sir Tristram. All people of every estate marvelled at his great deeds, and all shouted for "the Knight with the Black Shield!"

The uproar was so great that Sir Lancelot heard it, and getting a great spear he came towards the shouting. "Knight with the Black Shield, make ready to joust with me!" he cried.

When Sir Tristram heard this, he took spear in hand, and both lowered their heads and came together like thunder. Sir Tristram's spear broke in pieces, and Sir Lancelot by ill fortune struck Sir Tristram on the side, a deep wound nigh to death. But yet Sir Tristram left not his saddle, and so the spear broke. Though sorely wounded, Tristram got out his sword and rushed at Sir Lancelot and gave him three great strokes on the helmet, so that sparks flew out, and Sir Lancelot lowered his head down to his saddlebow. And then Sir Tristram departed from the field, for he felt himself so wounded that he thought he should die.

Sir Dinadan saw him go and followed him into the forest. After they had gone some way, Sir Tristram alighted, and unlaced his harness and dressed his wound. Then Sir Dinadan feared that he would die.

"Nay, nay, Dinadan, never dread," said Sir Tristram, "for I am heart whole, and of this wound I shall soon be healed, by the mercy of God."

When Sir Tristram departed into the forest, Sir Lancelot held always the fight, like a man enraged, who took no heed to himself, and there was many a noble knight against him. King Arthur, seeing Sir Lancelot do such marvellous deeds of arms, armed himself, and taking his horse and armour, rode into the field to help Sir Lancelot, and many other knights came in with King Arthur. To make a short tale, in conclusion, the king of North Wales and the King of the Hundred Knights were put to the worse, and because Sir Lancelot remained, and was the last in the field, the prize was given him.

Sir Lancelot, however, would not for king, queen, nor knight accept the prize, but wherever the cry was cried through the field, "Sir Lancelot, Sir Lancelot has won the field this day!" Sir Lancelot had another contrary cry made—"Sir Tristram has won the field! For he began first, and last he has endured! And so he has done the first day, the second, and the third day!"

The Quest of the Ten Knights

Then every one, high and low, said great things of Sir Lancelot for the honour he did Sir Tristram, and because of that honour done to Sir Tristram he was at that time more praised and renowned than if he had overthrown five hundred knights. And all the people, solely because of this courtesy, first the nobles, great and small, and afterwards all the common folk, cried at once, "Sir Lancelot has won the field, whoever says nay!" At this Lancelot was angry and ashamed, and therewith he rode to King Arthur.

"Alas!" said the king, "we are all dismayed that Sir Tristram is thus departed from us. Truly he is one of the noblest knights that ever I saw hold spear or sword in hand."

King Arthur and Sir Lancelot took their horses to seek Sir Tristram, but when they came to the pavilion where he had slept the night before the tournament, he and Sir Dinadan were gone. They returned to the Castle of Maidens, making great grief for the hurt of Sir Tristram and his sudden departing.

Right so came Sir Gaheris, and told King Arthur that after Sir Tristram was wounded Sir Palamides had gone after him into the forest and challenged him to joust, and that Sir Tristram had there struck him down.

"Alas," said King Arthur, "that was great dishonour to Sir Palamides, inasmuch as Sir Tristram was sorely wounded, and now may we all, kings, knights and men of worship, say that Sir Tristram may be called a noble knight, and one of the best knights I ever saw. I never saw knight do so marvellously as he has done these three days; for he was the first who began, and the longest who held on, save this last day. And though he was hurt, it was a manly adventure of two noble knights."

"As for me," said Sir Lancelot, "for all the lands that ever my father left me, I would not have hurt Sir Tristram if I had known him at that time. That I hurt him was because I saw not his shield, for if I had seen his black shield I would not have meddled with him, for he did lately for me as much as ever knight did; and it is well known that he had ado with thirty knights, and no help save Sir Dinadan. And one thing I shall promise—Sir Palamides shall repent it for his unkindly dealing in following that noble knight, whom I by mishap hurt."

Then King Arthur made a great feast, and at the feast he said to Sir Lancelot: "Had it not been for you we had not lost Sir Tristram, for he was here daily until the time you met with him."

Then Sir Lancelot said: "Here we are, ten knights who will swear never to rest one night where we rest another, this twelve months, until we find Sir Tristram. And as for me, I promise you that if I meet with him, by fair means or foul, I shall bring him to this court, or else I shall die for it."

The names of the ten knights who undertook this quest were these: First was Sir Lancelot; then Sir Ector de Maris, Sir Bors de Ganis, Bleoberis, and Sir Blamor de Ganis; Lucas, the butler; Sir Uwaine, Sir Galihud, Sir Lionel, and Galiodin.

These ten noble knights departed from the court of King Arthur, and thus they rode upon their quest together, until they came to a cross, where parted four highways; and there the fellowship broke up into four parties to seek Sir Tristram.

In the meanwhile, Sir Tristram and Sir Dinadan were lodging in the castle of an old knight called Sir Darras.

Sir Palamides after his fall in the forest was nearly out of his wits with rage against Sir Tristram, so he resolved to follow him. Coming to a river, in his madness he tried to make his horse leap over, but his horse failed footing and fell into the river, wherefore Sir Palamides dreaded lest he should be drowned. However, he got clear from his horse and swam to the land, but the horse went down in the water.

When Sir Palamides reached the land, he took off his armour and sat roaring and crying like a man out of his mind. Right so came a damsel past Sir Palamides, and he and she had language together, which pleased neither of them; so the damsel rode her way till she came to the place where Tristram was lodging with the old knight, and there she told him how by chance she had met with the maddest knight that ever she had met.

"What bore he on his shield?" said Sir Tristram.

"It was indented with white and black," said the damsel.

"Ah," said Sir Tristram, "that is Sir Palamides, the good knight, for well I know him for one of the best knights living in this realm."

Then the old knight took a little horse, and rode for Sir Palamides and brought him to his own manor.

When Sir Palamides saw Sir Tristram, he looked at him curiously, for although he did not recognize him, it seemed to him he had seen him before. Then he would say to Sir Dinadan, "If ever I may meet with Sir Tristram, he shall not escape my hands."

"I marvel," said Sir Dinadan, "that you boast behind Sir Tristram's back, for it is but lately he was in your hands. Why would you not hold him when you had him? For I myself saw twice or thrice that you got but little worship of Sir Tristram."

Then was Sir Palamides ashamed.

Thus they stayed for awhile in the castle with the old knight, Sir Darras. But one day there came a damsel who told Sir Darras that three of his sons had been slain at the tournament of the Castle of Maidens, and two grievously wounded, so that they were never likely to help themselves, and all this was done by a noble knight who bore a black shield. Then someone else said that the same knight who bore the black shield was now within that very castle. Sir Darras went to Tristram's chamber, and there he found his shield and showed it to the damsel.

"Ah, sir," said the damsel, "the same man who bore that shield is he who slew your three sons."

Sir Darras at once threw Sir Tristram, and Sir Palamides, and Sir Dinadan into a strong prison, and there Sir Tristram endured great pain, for sickness overtook him, and that is the greatest pain a prisoner can have. For all the while a prisoner has his health of body, he can endure by the mercy of God and in hope of good deliverance, but when sickness touches a prisoner's body, then may a prisoner say all wealth is bereft him.

The Strange Shield of Morgan le Fay

When Sir Tristram fell so ill, Sir Dinadan and Sir Palamides made great sorrow, and one day a damsel came and found them mourning. So she went to Sir Darras and told him how the mighty knight who bore the black shield was likely to die.

"That shall not be," said Sir Darras, "for God forbid that when any knights come to me for succour I should suffer them to die within my prison. Therefore, fetch that knight and his companions before me." And when he saw Tristram he said, "Sir Knight, I repent me of your sickness, for you are called a full noble knight, and so you seem. And it shall never be said that Sir Darras shall destroy such a noble knight as you are in prison, howbeit you have slain three of my sons, whereby I was greatly aggrieved. But now you shall go and your companions. Your armour and horses have been fair and clean kept, and you shall go where you like—upon this covenant, that you, knight, will promise me to be good friend to my two sons who are now alive, and also that you tell me your name."

"Sir," said he, "as for me, my name is Sir Tristram of Lyonesse, and in Cornwall was I born, and I am nephew to King Mark. And as for the death of your sons, I could not help it, for if they had been the next kin that I have, I could not have done otherwise. If indeed I had slain them by treason or treachery, I had been worthy to have died. But I promise you by the faith of my body I will do you service as long as I live, for you have done to us only as a knight would naturally do."

Sir Tristram rested in the castle till his sickness mended, and when he was well again and strong, the three companions made ready to leave. Every knight took his horse, and so they departed, riding together till they came to a crossways, where they each went a different road.

It happened by chance that Sir Tristram came to ask for lodging at a castle where Morgan le Fay was, and there that night he had good cheer. On the morrow when he would have departed, the queen said: "Know well, you shall not depart lightly, for you are here as a prisoner."

"God forbid," said Sir Tristram, "for I was but lately a prisoner."

"Fair knight," said the queen, "you shall abide with me till I know what you are and whence you come. Tell me your name, and I will suffer you to depart when you will."

"Upon that covenant I will tell you my name—it is Sir Tristram of Lyonesse."

"Ah," said Morgan le Fay, "if I had known that, you should not have departed so soon, but since I have made a promise I will keep it, on condition that you will promise me to bear a shield that I shall deliver you to the Castle of the Hard Rock, where King Arthur has proclaimed a great tournament, and I pray you to go there and do for me as much deeds of arms as you can do."

"Madam," said Tristram, "let me see the shield that I shall bear."

So the shield was brought forth, and it was goldish, with a king and queen painted thereon, and a knight standing above them, with one foot on the king's head and the other upon the queen's.

"Madam," said Tristram, "that is a fair shield and a mighty, but what signifies this king and this queen, and that knight standing upon both their heads?"

"I will tell you," said Morgan le Fay. "It signifies King Arthur and Queen Guinevere, and a knight that holds them both in bondage."

"Who is that knight?" asked Tristram.

"That you shall not know just yet," said the queen.

But it was a wicked device of Morgan le Fay to bring trouble on Sir Lancelot out of revenge, because he would never love her nor do anything at her request. She hoped King Arthur would see the shield and be angry with Sir Lancelot because of the picture on it.

Taking leave of the queen, Sir Tristram rode to the castle, where he saw five hundred tents. The king of Scots and the king of Ireland held against King Arthur's knights, and there began a great *mêlée*. Sir Tristram rushed into the fray and did marvellous deeds of arms, striking down many knights. And always in the front of the fight shone that strange shield.

When the king saw it he marvelled greatly with what intent it had been made, but Queen Guinevere guessed what it was and was heavy-hearted. A damsel of Queen Morgan le Fay's happened to be present in the chamber from which the king watched the tournament, and when she heard him speak of the shield, she said openly: "Sir King, know you well that this shield was ordained for you, to show you shame and dishonour," and then she stole away secretly, so that no man knew what became of her.

King Arthur was sad and angry at her words, and asked from whence came that damsel, but there was no one who knew her nor where she went.

All this while the king watched Sir Tristram, who did such marvellous deeds of arms that he wondered sorely what knight he could be, for he knew well it was not Sir Lancelot. He was told that Sir Tristram was in Brittany with his wife, Iseult of the White Hands, for if he had been in England Arthur thought Sir Lancelot or some of his companions who had gone in quest of Sir Tristram would have found him before now. So King Arthur marvelled what knight this could be, and he kept always gazing at the shield.

Then Sir Tristram struck down knights, wonderful to behold, on the right and on the left, scarcely a knight could withstand him. But the king of Scots and the king of Ireland began to withdraw themselves. Arthur, seeing this, resolved that the knight with the strange shield should not escape him. Therefore he called Sir Uwaine, and bade him arm and make ready; and they quickly appeared before Sir Tristram and challenged him to tell them from where he had the shield.

"Sir," he said, "I had it from Queen Morgan le Fay, sister to King Arthur."

"If you can describe what you bear, you are worthy to bear the arms."

"As for that," said Sir Tristram, "I will answer you. This shield was given me, not desired, by Queen Morgan le Fay. And as for me, I cannot describe these arms, for it is no point of my charge, and yet I trust to bear them with honour."

"Truly," said King Arthur, "you ought to bear no arms unless you know what you bear. But I pray you tell me your name."

"To what intent?" said Sir Tristram.

"Because I wish to know it," said King Arthur.

"Sir, you shall not know it at this time."

"Then shall you and I do battle together," said King Arthur.

"Why will you do battle with me unless I tell you my name?" said Tristram. "You need hardly do that, if you were a man of honour, for you have seen me this day have great travail; therefore you are an unworthy knight to ask battle of me. However, I will not fail you, and do not imagine that I fear you; though you think you have me at a great advantage, yet I shall endure right well."

Then King Arthur dressed his shield and his spear, and Sir Tristram against him, and they came so eagerly together that King Arthur broke his spear to pieces upon Sir Tristram's shield. But Sir Tristram hit King Arthur again, so that horse and man fell to the earth, and the king was wounded on the left side, a great wound and perilous.

When Sir Uwaine saw his lord Arthur lie on the ground sore wounded, he was sad. Then he dressed his shield and spear, and cried aloud to Sir Tristram, "Knight, defend yourself!" They came together like thunder, and Sir Uwaine broke his spear to pieces on Tristram's shield. And Sir Tristram struck him harder and sorer, with such might that he bore him clean out of his saddle to the earth.

With that, Sir Tristram turned about and said: "Fair knights, I had no need to joust with you, for I have had enough to do this day."

Then Arthur arose and went to Sir Uwaine, and said to Sir Tristram: "We have as we have deserved, for through our pride we demanded battle of you, and yet we knew not your name."

The Tombstone by the River of Camelot

After overthrowing King Arthur and Sir Uwaine, Sir Tristram departed from the Castle of the Hard Rock. Everywhere he went he asked after Sir Lancelot, but in no place could he hear of him, whether he were dead or alive, wherefore Sir Tristram made great grief and sorrow. As he rode by a forest he was aware of a fair tower with a marsh on one side and a green meadow on the other, and there he saw ten knights fighting together. As he came nearer, he saw how it was but one knight who did battle against nine knights, and that one knight did so marvellously that Tristram wondered greatly how one knight could do such deeds of arms. He had great pity for him, and by his shield he thought it must be Sir Palamides.

So he rode to the knights, and cried to them and bade them cease their battle, for they did themselves great shame, so many knights to fight with one.

The master of the party, who was Breuse Without Pity, the most mischievous knight then living, scornfully defied Sir Tristram, but when his men felt Sir Tristram's strokes they all fled into the tower, and though Tristram followed fast after, with his sword in his hand, they escaped and shut him outside the gates.

Sir Tristram returned to the knight he had rescued and found him sitting under a tree, sore wounded.

"Great thanks to you for your goodness," said the knight, "for you have saved my life."

"What is your name?" said Tristram.

He answered that it was Palamides.

"Oh," said Sir Tristram, "you have had a fair favour of me this day that I should rescue you, and you are the man in the world whom I most hate! But now make ready, for I will do battle with you."

"What is your name?" said Palamides.

"My name is Sir Tristram, your mortal enemy."

"It may be so," said Sir Palamides, "but you have done overmuch for me this day that I should fight with you; for inasmuch as you have saved my life it will be no honour for you to have ado with me, for you are fresh, and I am wounded sore. Therefore, if you will need have ado with me, assign me a day, and then I shall meet you without fail."

"You say well," said Sir Tristram. "Now I assign you to meet me, to do battle with me, this day fortnight, in the meadow by the river of Camelot, where Merlin set the tombstone."

"I shall not fail you," said Sir Palamides.

Thus they were agreed, and so they departed, each taking a different way.

At the time appointed Sir Tristram rode straight to Camelot, to the tomb which Merlin had made long before on the spot where the brave knight Lanceor and his fair lady Columbe were both buried under one stone. And at that time Merlin prophesied that in that same place should fight two of the best knights that were ever in Arthur's days.

When Tristram came to the tomb, he looked about him for Sir Palamides. Then he was aware of a comely knight who came riding against him, all in white, with a covered shield. When he came near, Sir Tristram cried, "You are welcome, Sir Knight, and well and truly have you kept your promise."

Then they dressed their shields and spears, and came together with all the might of their horses. They met so fiercely that both horses and knights fell to the earth, but freeing themselves as swiftly as they could, they struck together with bright swords, and each wounded the other sorely. Thus they fought for a long while, and many great pieces were hewn out of their armour, but never one word was uttered by either of them.

At last the knight clad in white spoke and said: "Knight, you fight wonderfully well, as ever I saw knight. Therefore, if it please you, tell me your name."

"Sir," said Tristram, "I am loath to tell any man my name."

"Truly," said the stranger, "if ever I were required, I was never loath to tell my name."

"It is well said," quoth Tristram, "then I require you to tell me your name."

"Fair knight," said he, "my name is Sir Lancelot of the Lake."

"Alas," said Tristram, "what have I done? For you are the man in the world I love the best."

"Fair knight," said Sir Lancelot, "tell me your name."

"Truly, my name is Sir Tristram."

"Oh," said Sir Lancelot, "what adventure is befallen me!" And he knelt down and yielded up his sword to Tristram. But Tristram, too, knelt down and yielded his sword to Lancelot, thus each gave the other the honour. And afterwards they rode to Camelot.

As they came near, they met Sir Gawaine and Sir Gaheris, who had promised King Arthur never to come again to the court till they brought Sir Tristram with them.

"Return again," said Lancelot, "for your quest is done, for I have met with Sir Tristram. Lo, here is he in person!"

Then was Sir Gawaine glad. "You are welcome," he said to Tristram, "for now have you eased me greatly of my labour."

At this moment came King Arthur, and when he knew that Sir Tristram was there, he ran to him, and taking him by the hand, said, "Sir Tristram, you are as welcome as any knight that ever came to this court," and so he led him to the Round Table.

Then came Queen Guinevere, and many ladies with her, and all the ladies said with one voice, "Welcome, Sir Tristram!"

"Welcome," said Arthur, "for one of the best knights and the gentlest of the world, and the man of most renown! For of all manner of hunting you bear the prize; and of all the terms of hunting and hawking you are the beginner; in all instruments of music you are the most skilled. Therefore, gentle knight," said Arthur, "you are welcome to this court! Also, I pray you, grant me a boon."

"It shall be at your command," said Tristram.

"Well," said Arthur, "I desire of you that you will abide in my court."

"Sir," said Tristram, "I am loath to do that, for I have ado in many countries."

"Not so," said Arthur. "You have promised it me; you cannot say nay."

"Sir, I will do as you will," said Tristram.

Arthur went to the seats about the Round Table, and looked in all the seats where knights were lacking. Then the King saw in the seat of Sir Marhaus letters which said: "This is the seat of the noble knight, Sir Tristram."

So with great splendour and feasting, King Arthur made Sir Tristram Knight of the Round Table.

THE QUEST OF THE HOLY GRAIL

The Siege Perilous

Now we will leave Sir Tristram of Lyonesse, and speak of Sir Lancelot of the Lake, and Sir Galahad, Sir Lancelot's son.

Before the time when Galahad was born there came a hermit to King Arthur, on Whitsunday, as the knights sat at the Round Table. Now there was one seat at the Round Table which always stood empty, and it was called "the Siege Perilous". When the hermit saw this seat he asked the king and all the knights why it was empty.

"There is never anyone who shall sit in that seat without being destroyed, except one person," was the answer.

"Do you know who that is ?" asked the hermit.

"Nay," said Arthur, and all the knights, "we know not who he is that shall sit therein."

"Then I know," said the hermit. "He that shall sit there is not yet born; and this year, he that is to sit there, in the Siege Perilous, shall be born. And he shall win the Holy Grail."

When the hermit said this he departed from the court of King Arthur.

After this feast Sir Lancelot rode on his adventures, till one day by chance he passed over the bridge of Corbin, and there he saw the fairest tower he had ever seen, and under it was a beautiful town full of people; and all the people, men and women, cried at once: "Welcome, Sir Lancelot of the Lake, flower of all knighthood, for by you we shall be helped out of danger."

Sir Lancelot asked why they thus called upon him, whereupon the people replied that a fair lady was cruelly shut up in a hot room in the tower, and no one but himself could deliver her. Sir Lancelot, therefore, went to the tower, and when he came to the chamber where the lady was, the iron doors unlocked and unbolted themselves. He went into the room, which was as hot as any furnace, and there he found a beautiful lady, and he took her by the hand. By enchantment Queen Morgan le Fay and the queen of North Wales had put her into this hot room, because she was called the fairest lady of that country. There she had been five years, and never might be delivered out of her pain until the time when the best knight of the world had taken her by the hand.

When she found herself rescued from the wicked spell, the lady asked Sir Lancelot to go with her into a church, to give God thanks for her deliverance. This having been done, and all the people, learned and unlearned, having given thanks, they said to Lancelot, "Sir Knight, since you have delivered this lady, you shall deliver us from a serpent that is here in a tomb."

Sir Lancelot took his shield, and said, "Bring me thither, and what I can do to please God and yourselves, that will I do."

The people led him to the place, and there he saw written on the tomb letters of gold, which said thus: "Here shall come a leopard of king's blood, and he shall slay this serpent, and this leopard shall have a son, a lion, in this foreign country; the which lion shall pass all other knights."

Sir Lancelot lifted up the tomb, and out sprang a horrible and fiendish dragon, spitting fire from his mouth. The dragon flew at Sir Lancelot, but the knight fell upon him with his sword, and at last, after a long fight, with great pain he slew him.

Therewith came King Pelles, the good and noble knight, and saluted Sir Lancelot, and he him again.

"Fair knight," said the king, "what is your name?"

"Sir, know you well, my name is Lancelot of the Lake."

"And my name," said the king, "is Pelles, king of this country, and I am of the family of Joseph of Arimathea."

Then each made much of the other, and so they went into the castle to take their repast. And straightway there came in a dove at a window, and in her mouth a little censer of gold. Immediately there was such a savour as if all the spices of the world had been there, and forthwith on the table were all manner of meats and drinks.

Then in came a damsel, passing young and fair, and she bore a vessel of gold between her hands. The king knelt down devoutly and said his prayers, and so did all who were there.

"What may this mean?" said Sir Lancelot.

"That is the most precious thing that ever living man has," said King Pelles. "And when the fame of this thing goes about, the Round Table shall be broken. Know you well, this is the Holy Grail that you have seen."

Now King Pelles had a daughter, as fair a lady, and young, and as wise as any at that time living. Her name was Elaine. When Sir Lancelot slew the dragon, King Pelles knew that the words written in letters of gold on the tomb would come true. For "the leopard of king's blood" who came into the foreign country meant Sir Lancelot himself, and "the lion" who was to surpass all other knights was Sir Galahad, who was no other than the son of Sir Lancelot of the Lake and the Lady Elaine, daughter of King Pelles.

How Galahad was made Knight

Fifteen years had gone by since that Whitsunday when King Arthur and his knights held festival at Camelot, and the hermit had foretold who it was that was to sit in the Siege Perilous. Once again it was the vigil of Pentecost, when all the fellowship of the Round Table had come to Camelot to renew their vows and take part in the holy service. The tables were set ready for the feast when right into the hall entered a fair gentlewoman, who had ridden full fast, for her horse was covered with sweat.

She alighted, and came before King Arthur and saluted him, and he said, "Damsel, God bless you!"

"Sir," she said, "I pray you tell me where Sir Lancelot is."

"Yonder you may see him," said the king.

Then she went to Lancelot and said, "Sir Lancelot, I salute you on King Pelles's behalf, and I require you to come with me to a forest hereby."

"What will you with me?" asked Sir Lancelot.

"You shall know when you come thither."

"Well," said he, "I will gladly go with you."

So Sir Lancelot bade his squire saddle his horse and bring his arms, and so he departed with the gentlewoman. They rode until they came to a forest and into a great valley, where they saw an abbey of nuns. A squire was ready who opened the gates, so they entered and descended off their horses, and a fair company came about Sir Lancelot, and welcomed him.

They led him into the abbess's chamber and unarmed him, and there he found two of his cousins, Sir Bors and Sir Lionel, who were greatly rejoiced and astonished to see him.

As they stood talking together, there came twelve nuns, who brought with them a boy of about fifteen years old, so beautiful and well made that scarcely in the world could man find his match. And all those ladies were weeping.

"Sir," they said, "we bring you here this child, Galahad, whom we have nourished, and we pray you to make him a knight; for of no worthier man's hand could he receive the order of knighthood."

Sir Lancelot beheld that young squire, and saw him seemly and demure as a dove, with all manner of good features, so that he thought he had never seen a man of his age so fair of face and form.

Then said Sir Lancelot, "Comes this desire of himself?"

And the boy and all the nuns said "Yea!"

"Then shall he receive the high order of knighthood tomorrow at the reverence of the high feast," said Lancelot.

That night Sir Lancelot had good cheer, and on the morrow, at the hour of dawn, at Galahad's desire he made him knight.

"God make you a good man," said Sir Lancelot, "for beauty fails you not, as any that lives. Now, fair sir, will you come with me to the court of King Arthur?"

"Nay," said the boy, "I will not go with you at this time."

So Sir Lancelot departed from the abbey and took his two cousins with him, and they came to Camelot by nine o'clock in the morning on Whitsunday. By that time the king and the queen had gone to holy service. When the king and the knights came back, the barons saw that the seats of the Round Table were all written about with gold letters—here one ought to sit, and here ought another to sit.

Thus they went along until they came to the Siege Perilous, where they found letters of gold, newly written, which said: "Four hundred winters and fifty-four after the passion of our Lord Jesus Christ, ought this Siege to be filled."

Then they all said, "This is a marvellous thing."

"By heaven it is," said Sir Lancelot, and then he counted the period of the writing from the time of our Lord to that day. "It seems to me," he said, "this siege ought to be filled this same day, for this is the Feast of Pentecost after the four hundredth and fifty-fourth year. And if it would please all parties, I counsel that none of these letters be seen this day until he comes who ought to achieve this adventure."

Then they ordered a cloth of silk to be brought to cover these letters in the Siege Perilous, after which King Arthur bade them haste to dinner.

"Sir," said Sir Kay, the steward, "if you go now to your meat, you will break the old custom of your court. For you are not used on this day to sit down to table before you have seen some adventure."

"You speak truth," said the king, "but I had so great joy of Sir Lancelot, and of his cousins, who are come to the court whole and sound, that I thought not of my old custom."

As they stood speaking, in came a squire.

"Sir," he said to the king, "I bring to you marvellous tidings."

"What are they?" said the king.

"Sir, there is here beneath, at the river, a great stone, which I saw float above the water, and therein I saw sticking a sword."

"I will see that marvel," said the king.

So all the knights went with him, and when they came to the river, they found there a stone floating, and therein stuck a fair and rich sword, in the pommel of which were precious stones, wrought with subtle letters of gold.

Then the barons read the letters, which said: "Never shall man take me hence but he by whose side I ought to hang, and he shall be the best knight of the world."

When King Arthur saw these letters he said to Sir Lancelot: "Fair sir, this sword ought to be yours, for I am sure you are the best knight in the world."

But Sir Lancelot answered full soberly: "Certain, sir, it is not my sword. Also, know you well, I have no hardihood to set my hand to it, for it belongs not to hang by my side. Also, whoever attempts to take that sword, and fails, he shall receive from it a wound of which long afterwards he shall not be whole. And I will that you take note that this same day the adventure of the Holy Grail will begin."

Marvels, and Greater Marvels

Then King Arthur asked his nephew Sir Gawaine to try to draw the sword from the stone in the river. But Sir Gawaine said he could not do it. Then the king commanded him to make the attempt.

"Sir," said Gawaine, "since you command me, I will obey." Then he took the sword by the handle, but he could not stir it.

"I thank you," said the king.

"My lord Sir Gawaine," said Sir Lancelot, "now know you well, this sword shall touch you so sore that you shall wish you had never set your hand to it, for the best castle of this realm."

"I could not withstay my uncle's will and command," said Gawaine.

King Arthur, hearing this, repented greatly what he had done, nevertheless he asked Sir Percival to attempt it, for his love.

"Gladly, to bear Sir Gawaine fellowship," replied Sir Percival, and he set his hand on the sword and drew it strongly, but he could not move it. Then there were others who dared to be so bold as to set their hands to it.

"Now you may go to your dinner," said Sir Kay to the king, "for a marvellous adventure have you seen."

When they were served and the seats filled, save only the Siege Perilous, suddenly all the doors and windows shut of themselves. Yet the hall was not greatly darkened because of this, and they were one and all amazed.

King Arthur was the first to speak. "Fair fellows and lords," he said, "we have seen this day marvels, but before night I expect we shall see greater marvels."

In the meanwhile came in a good old man, very ancient, clothed all in white, and no knight knew from whence he came. He brought with him a young knight, also on foot, in red armour, without sword or shield, but with only a scabbard hanging by his side.

"Peace be with you, lords!" said the old man. Then to Arthur, "Sir, I bring here a young knight, who is of king's lineage, and of the kindred of Joseph of Arimathea, whereby the marvels of this court and of strange realms shall be fully accomplished."

The king was very pleased and said to the old man, "Sir, you are right welcome, and the young knight with you."

The old man made the young knight take off his armour, and under it he was clad in a coat of red silk, and the old man put on him a mantle furred with ermine. Then saying to the young knight, "Sir, follow me," he led him straight to the Siege Perilous, beside which sat Sir Lancelot. The good man lifted up the silken cloth, and underneath it he found letters which said: "This is the seat of Galahad, the high prince."

"Sir, know you well that place is yours," said the old man, and he made him sit down surely in that seat.

Then the young knight said to the old man, "Sir, you may now go your way, for you have done well what you were commanded to do. And commend me to my grandsire, King Pelles, and say to him on my behalf that I will come and see him as soon as ever I can."

So the good man departed.

All the Knights of the Round Table marvelled greatly at Galahad, because he had dared to sit in the Siege Perilous, and he was so tender of age. They knew not from whence he came, but only that God had sent him, and they said: "This is he by whom the Holy Grail shall be achieved, for never anyone but he sat in that place without mischief befalling."

But Sir Lancelot beheld his son, and had great joy of him.

Then King Arthur went to Galahad and said, "Sir, you are welcome, for you shall move many good knights to the quest of the Holy Grail, and you shall achieve that which never knight could do." Then the king took him by the hand and went down from the palace to show Galahad the adventure of the stone in the river.

"Here is as great a marvel as ever I saw," said King Arthur to Galahad, "and right good knights have attempted and failed."

"Sir, that is no marvel," said Galahad, "for this adventure is not theirs but mine, and with the certainty of this sword, I brought none with me, for here by my side hangs the scabbard." He laid his hand on the sword and lightly drew it out of the stone, and put it in the sheath.

"God will send you a shield," said the king.

"Now have I that sword which was sometime that good knight's, Balin the Savage," said Galahad, "and he was a good man of his hands. With this sword he slew his unknown brother Balan, and that was a great pity, for he was a good knight; and each slew the other, not knowing they were brothers, because of a dolorous stroke that Balan gave my grandfather, King Pelles, which is not yet whole, nor shall be till I heal him."

At that moment the king and all saw a lady on a white horse, who came riding down the river towards them. She saluted the king and the queen, and asked if Sir Lancelot were there. He answered himself, "I am here, fair lady."

Then she said, all weeping: "How your great doing is changed since this day in the morning!"

"Damsel, why say you so ?" said Lancelot.

"I say the truth," said the damsel, "for this morning you were the best knight in the world, but who should say so now would be a liar, for now there is one better than you."

"As touching that," said Sir Lancelot, "I know well I was never the best."

"Yes," said the damsel, "that you were and are so yet, of any sinful man of the world. And, Sir King, Nacien the hermit sends you word that there shall befall you the greatest honour that ever befell king in Britain. And I will tell you wherefore. This day the Holy Grail shall appear in your house, and feed you and all your fellowship of the Round Table."

So the damsel departed and went back the same way that she had come.

The Last Tournament

"Now," said King Arthur, "I am sure that all you of the Round Table will depart on this quest of the Holy Grail, and never shall I see the whole of you again all together. Therefore will I see you all together in the meadow of Camelot, to joust, that after your death men may speak of it, that such knights were wholly together on such a day."

So they all assembled in the meadow, and the queen was in a tower with all her ladies to behold that tournament. Then Galahad, at the king's entreaty, put on a noble cuirass, and also his helmet, but shield he would take none, not for any entreaty of the king.

Sir Gawaine and the other knights prayed him to take a spear, and this he did. Then taking his place in the middle of the meadow he began to break spears marvellously, so that all men wondered at him. For he there surpassed all other knights, and in a little while had thrown down many good Knights of the Round Table. But Sir Lancelot and Sir Percival he did not overthrow.

King Arthur, at Queen Guinevere's request, made him alight and unlace his helmet so that the queen might see his face. And when she beheld him she said, "Truly I dare well say that Sir Lancelot is his father, for never two men were more alike. Therefore it is no marvel if he be of great prowess."

Then the king and all the nobles went home to Camelot, and after they had been to evensong, they went to supper, and every knight sat in his own place as they had done before.

Suddenly they heard cracking and rolling of thunder, as if the place would have been riven. In the midst of this blast entered a sunbeam, clearer by seven times than ever they saw by day, and all their faces shone with a divine light. Then began every knight to look at each other, and each seemed fairer than anyone had seemed before. Not a knight could speak a single word for a great while, so they looked every man at each other, as if they had been dumb.

Then there entered into the hall the Holy Grail, covered with white silk, but none could see it, nor who bore it. And all the hall was filled with good odours, and every knight had such meats and drinks as he liked best; and when the Holy Grail had been borne through the hall, then the holy vessel departed suddenly, so that they knew not what became of it.

After it had gone they all had breath to speak, and King Arthur gave thanks to God for the great favour He had sent them.

"Now," said Sir Gawaine, "we have been served this day with what meats and drinks we thought of, but one thing has failed us— we could not see the Holy Grail, it was covered with such care. Therefore I will here make a vow, that tomorrow without longer abiding I shall undertake the Quest of the Holy Grail. I shall hold out a twelvemonth and a day, or more, if need be, and never shall I return again to the court till I have seen it more openly than it has been seen here. And if I do not succeed, I shall return again as one that cannot act against the will of heaven."

When the Knights of the Round Table heard what Sir Gawaine said, most of them rose up and made the same sort of vow as Sir Gawaine had made.

King Arthur was greatly displeased at this, for he knew well they might not gainsay their vows.

"Alas," he said to Sir Gawaine, "you have bereft me of the fairest fellowship, and the truest of knighthood that ever were seen together in any realm of the world. For when my knights depart hence I am sure that never more will they all meet together in this world, for many of them shall die in the Quest."

And therewith his eyes filled with tears.

"Comfort yourself," said Lancelot, "for if we die in the Quest it shall be to us as a great honour, and much more than if we had died in any other place; for, early or late, of death we are sure."

"Ah, Lancelot," said the king, "the great love I have had for you all the days of my life makes me say such grievous words. For never Christian king had so many worthy men at his table as I have had this day at the Round Table, and that is my great sorrow."

All the court were troubled because of the departing of those knights. Some of the ladies who loved knights wanted to go with their husbands and lovers, and would have done so had not an aged knight in religious clothing come among them.

"Fair lords, who have sworn to the Quest of the Holy Grail," he said, "Nacien the hermit thus sends you word that none in this Quest lead lady or gentlewoman, for it is a hard and high service. And, moreover, I warn you plainly that he who is not clean of his sins shall not see these mysteries."

After this, the queen came to Galahad and asked him whence he was and of what country. He told her.

"And son unto Lancelot?" she asked, but to this he said neither yea nor nay.

"Truly," said the queen, "of your father you need not be ashamed, for he is the goodliest knight, and come of the best men of the world, on both sides of a race of kings. Wherefore you ought of right to be of your deeds a good man—and certainly you resemble him much."

Galahad was a little abashed at this, and said: "Madam, since you know it for certain, why did you ask me? For he that is my father shall be known openly, and in good time."

Then they all went to rest. And in honour of Galahad's greatness and high race he was led into King Arthur's chamber, and rested on the king's own bed.

As soon as it was day the king arose, for he had no rest all that night for sorrow, and then he and the queen went to church.

Lancelot and Gawaine commanded their men to bring their arms, and when they were all armed save their shields and their helmets, they were ready in the same wise to go to the church to hear the service.

After the service the king wished to know how many had undertaken the Quest of the Holy Grail, and they found by counting it was a hundred and fifty, and all were Knights of the Round Table.

Then they put on their helmets ready to depart, and commended them all wholly to the queen, and there was weeping and great sorrow. And Queen Guinevere went into her chamber, so that no one should see her great grief

Sir Lancelot, missing the queen, went to look for her, and when she saw him, she cried aloud: "O, Sir Lancelot, you have forsaken us! You put me to death thus to leave my lord!"

"Ah, madam," said Sir Lancelot, "I pray you be not displeased, for I shall come again as soon as I can in accordance with my honour."

"Alas," said she, "that ever I saw you! But He that suffered death upon the Cross for all mankind be your good conduct and safety, and that of all the whole fellowship!"

Right so departed Sir Lancelot, and found his companions who awaited his coming. They mounted their horses and rode through the streets of Camelot, and there was weeping of the rich and poor, and the king turned away, and could not speak for weeping.

So the Knights of the Round Table rode forth on the Quest of the Holy Grail.

That night they rested in a castle called Vagon, where the lord was a good old man and made them the best cheer he could. On the morrow they all agreed they should each separate from the other. So the next day, with weeping and mourning, they departed, and every knight took the way that seemed to him best.

Sir Galahad's White Shield

Now Galahad was yet without a shield, and he rode four days without adventure.

On the fourth day after evensong he came to an abbey of white friars, and there he was received with great reverence and led to a chamber, and unarmed. Then he was aware of two Knights of the Round Table, one was King Bagdemagus, the other was Sir Uwaine, and they were very pleased to see him.

"Sirs," said Galahad, "what adventures brought you hither?"

"It is told us," they replied, "that in this place is a shield that no man may bear about his neck without being hurt or dead within three days, or else maimed for ever."

"I shall bear it tomorrow to attempt this strange adventure," added King Bagdemagus to Galahad, "and if I cannot achieve this adventure of the shield, you shall take it upon you, for I am sure you shall not fail."

"I agree right well to that," said Galahad, "for I have no shield."

On the morrow they arose, and after hearing service, King Bagdemagus asked where the shield was. A monk at once led him behind an altar, where the shield hung. It was white as any snow but in the midst was a red cross.

"Sir," said the monk, "this shield ought not to hang round the neck of any knight unless he be the worthiest knight of the world; therefore I counsel you knights to be well advised."

"Well," said King Bagdemagus, "I know well I am not the best knight of the world, but yet I shall try to bear it."

So he bore it out of the monastery, saying to Galahad, "If it please you, I pray you abide here still, till you know how I shall fare."

"I will await you here," said Galahad.

King Bagdemagus took with him a squire to carry back tidings to Galahad how he fared. When they had ridden about two miles they came to a fair valley before a hermitage, and there they saw coming from that direction a goodly knight, in white armour, horse and all. He came as fast as his horse could run, with his spear levelled, and King Bagdemagus dressed his spear against him and broke it upon the white knight. But the other struck him so hard that he shattered the mail and thrust him through the right shoulder, for just there the shield did not cover him, and so he bore him from his horse.

Then the knight alighted and took the white shield from Bagdemagus, saying: "Knight, you have done yourself great folly, for this shield ought not to be borne but by him that shall have no peer that lives."

Then he came to King Bagdemagus's squire and said, "Bear this shield to the good knight Sir Galahad, whom you left in the abbey, and greet him well from me."

"Sir," said the squire, "what is your name?"

"Take you no heed of my name," said the knight, "for it is not for you to know, nor any earthly man."

"Now, fair sir," said the squire, "for the love of heaven, tell me for what cause this shield may not be borne without the bearer coming to mischief."

"Since you have conjured me so," said the knight, "this shield belongs to no man but Galahad."

The squire went to King Bagdemagus and asked if he were sore wounded or not.

"Yes, forsooth," he said, "I shall hardly escape death."

The squire fetched his horse and took him with great pain to an abbey. There he was gently unarmed and laid in a bed, and his wounds were looked to. And there he lay a long while and hardly escaped with life.

The squire carried the shield to Galahad, with the knight's message.

"Now blessed be God and fortune," said Galahad. Then he asked for his armour and mounted his horse, and hung the white shield about his neck and bade them goodbye. Sir Uwaine said he would bear him fellowship if it pleased him, but Galahad replied that he could not do so, for he must go alone except for the squire that went with him.

Within a little while Sir Galahad came near the hermitage, and there was the white knight awaiting him. Each saluted the other courteously, and then the strange knight told him the legend of the white shield.

It had been made over four hundred years ago by Joseph of Arimathea for a king called Evelake, who was at war with the Saracens. On the eve of a great battle, Joseph of Arimathea went to King Evelake and showed him the right belief of the Christian faith, to which he agreed with all his heart. Then this shield was made for King Evelake, and through it he got the better of his enemies. For when he went into battle there was a cloth placed over the shield, and when he found himself in the greatest peril, he drew aside the cloth, and then his enemies saw the cross and were all discomfited.

Afterwards befell a strange marvel, for the cross on the shield vanished away, so that no man knew what became of it.

At the end of the war King Evelake was baptised, and so were most of the people in his city. And when Joseph of Arimathea departed, King Evelake insisted on going with him, whether he would or not. So it chanced they came to this land, which at that time was called Great Britain.

Not long after, Joseph of Arimathea fell ill and was like to die. King Evelake was deeply grieved and prayed him to leave some token of remembrance. "That will I do full gladly," said the holy man, and he bade him bring the shield, which was now quite white. Then with his own blood Joseph of Arimathea traced on it a red cross.

"Now you may see a remembrance that I love you," he said, "for you shall never see this shield but you shall think of me. And it shall be always as fresh as it is now. And never shall any man bear this shield round his neck but he shall repent it until the time that Galahad the good knight bear it, and the last of my lineage shall have it about his neck, and shall do many marvellous deeds."

"Now," said King Evelake, "where shall I put this shield that this worthy knight may have it?"

"You shall leave it there where Nacien the hermit shall be put after his death. For thither shall that good knight come the fifth day after he receives the order of knighthood."

"So that day which they appointed is this time that you have received the shield," said the knight to Galahad. "And in the same abbey lies Nacien the hermit. And you are grandson of King Pelles, who is of the race of Joseph of Arimathea."

And with that, the White Knight vanished away.

The Adventure of the Crown of Gold

As soon as the squire heard what the White Knight said to Sir Galahad, he alighted off his horse, and kneeling down at Galahad's feet, prayed that he might go with him till he had made him knight. "And that order, by the grace of God, shall be well held by me," he added. So Sir Galahad granted his petition. Then they returned to the abbey where they had come from, and great joy was made of Sir Galahad, and there he rested that night.

On the morrow he knighted the squire, and asked him his name and of what kindred he was come.

"Sir," said he, "men call me Melias of the Isle, and I am the son of the king of Denmark."

"Now, fair sir," said Galahad, "since you come of kings and queens, look you that knighthood be well set in you, for you ought to be a mirror to all chivalry."

"Sir, you say truth," said Melias. "But since you have made me a knight you must by rights grant me my first desire, if it is reasonable."

"That is true," said Galahad.

"Then will you suffer me to ride with you in this Quest of the Holy Grail?" asked Melias.

And Galahad granted it.

His armour, his spear and his horse were then brought to Sir Melias, but Sir Galahad and he rode forth all that week before they found any adventure.

On a Monday, in the morning, after leaving an abbey, they came to a cross which parted two ways, and on that cross were letters written, which said thus: "Now you knights errant, who go to seek knights adventurous, see here two ways: one way it is forbidden you to go, for none shall come out of that way again, unless he be a good man and a worthy knight; if you go this way on the left, you shall not there lightly win prowess, for you shall in this way be soon tried."

"Sir," said Melias to Galahad, "if it please you to suffer me to take this way on the left, tell me, for there I shall well test my strength."

"It were better you rode not that way," said Galahad, "for I deem I should escape better in that way than you."

"Nay, my lord, I pray you let me have that adventure."

"Take it, in heaven's name," said Galahad.

Then Melias rode into an old forest, through which he travelled two days and more, till he came to a green meadow where there was a fair lodge of boughs. And he saw in this lodge a chair, wherein was a crown of gold, subtly wrought. Also, there were cloths spread upon the ground, on which were many delicious meats.

Sir Melias beheld this adventure and thought it marvellous. He had no hunger, but he had great desire of the crown of gold, so he stooped down, took it up, and rode his way with it. Soon he saw a knight come riding after him, who said: "Knight, set down that crown of gold, which is not yours, and therefore defend yourself!"

"Fair Lord of Heaven, help and save Your new-made knight!" prayed Sir Melias.

Then they urged on their horses as fast as they could, and the other knight struck Sir Melias through his coat of mail, and through the left side, so that he fell to the earth nearly dead. The knight took the crown of gold and went his way, and Sir Melias lay still and had no power to stir.

In the meanwhile, by good fortune came Sir Galahad, and found him there in peril of death.

"Ah, Melias, who has wounded you?" he said. "It would have been better to have ridden the other way."

"Sir, for God's love let me not die in this forest," said Melias, "but bear me to the abbey here beside that I may be confessed and have heavenly comfort."

"It shall be done," said Galahad, "but where is he that has wounded you?"

At that moment Sir Galahad heard through the trees a loud cry— "Knight, keep you from me!"

"Ah, sir, beware!" said Melias, "for that is he who has slain me."

"Sir Knight, come at your peril!" answered Sir Galahad.

Then each turned towards the other, and they came together as fast as their horses could run, and Galahad struck the stranger so that his spear went through his shoulder, and bore him down off his horse, and in the falling Galahad's spear broke. With that, out came another knight from among the trees and broke a spear upon Galahad before ever he could turn. Then Galahad drew out his sword and struck off his left arm, whereupon the knight fled.

After chasing him for some distance, Sir Galahad returned to Melias, and placing him gently on his horse, sprang up behind and held him in his arms, and so brought him to the abbey. There his wound was carefully tended, and an old monk, who had once been a knight, told Sir Galahad he hoped it would be healed within about seven weeks. Sir Galahad was glad to hear this, and said he would stay at the abbey for three days.

At the end of that time he said, "Now I will depart, for I have much on hand; many good knights are full busy about it, and this knight and I were in the same Quest of the Holy Grail."

"For his sin was he thus wounded," said the good man. "And I marvel," he added to Melias, "how you dare take upon you so rich a thing as the high order of knighthood without clean confession, and that was the cause you were bitterly wounded. For the road on the right betokens the highway of our Lord Jesus Christ, and the way of a true, good liver. And the other road betokens the way of sinners and misbelievers. And when the devil saw your pride and presumption tempt you into the Quest of the Holy Grail, that made you to be overthrown, for it may not be achieved but by virtuous living.

"Also, the writing on the cross was a sign of heavenly deeds and of knightly deeds in God's works, and no knightly deeds in worldly works; and pride is head of all deadly sins which caused you, Melias, to depart from Sir Galahad. And when you took the crown of gold, you sinned in covetousness and theft. All these were no knightly deeds. And this Galahad, the holy knight, who fought with the two knights—the two knights signify the two deadly sins, pride and covetousness, which were wholly in Sir Melias, and they could not stand against Sir Galahad, for he is without deadly sin."

Now departed Galahad from them, and bade them all goodbye.

"My lord Galahad," said Melias, "as soon as I can ride I shall seek you."

"God send you health," said Galahad, and so took his horse and departed.

The Vision at the Chapel in the Forest

Sir Galahad rode till he came to a waste forest, and there he met with Sir Lancelot and Sir Percival, but they did not know him, for he was newly disguised. Sir Lancelot rode straight at him and broke his spear on him, and Sir Galahad struck him so again that he bore down horse and man. Then he drew his sword and turned to Sir Percival, and struck him on the helmet so that it rove to the coif of steel; if the sword had not swerved, Sir Percival would have been slain; with the stroke he fell out of the saddle.

This joust took place before a hermitage where dwelt a recluse, who was really aunt to Sir Percival, although he did not know it. When she saw Sir Galahad she said, "God be with you, best knight of the world! Ah, certain," she said quite loud, so that Lancelot and Percival could hear it, "if yonder two knights had known you as well as I do, they would not have encountered with you."

Galahad, hearing her say this, was afraid of being known and therefore rode swiftly away. Then both knights perceived he was Galahad, and up they got on their horses and rode fast after him, but he was soon out of sight. So they returned with heavy heart.

"Let us ask some tidings of yonder recluse," said Percival.

"Do so, if you please," said Lancelot, but when Percival went to the hermitage he rode on alone. This way and that he rode across a wild forest and held no path except as adventure led him. At last he came to a strong cross, which pointed two ways in waste land. By the cross was a stone that was of marble, but it was so dark that Sir Lancelot could not tell what it was.

Sir Lancelot looked about him, and near at hand he saw an old chapel, where he expected to find people. He tied his horse to a tree, and taking off his shield, hung it upon the tree. Then he went to the chapel door but found it waste and broken. And looking within, he saw a fair altar, full richly arrayed with cloth of clean silk, where stood a shining candlestick which bore six great candles, and the candlestick was of silver.

When Sir Lancelot saw this light he desired greatly to enter into the chapel, but could find no place where he could enter, which greatly grieved and perplexed him. He returned to his horse and took off the saddle and bridle, and let him pasture; and unlacing his helmet and ungirding his sword, he laid himself down to sleep on his shield before the marble cross.

So he fell asleep, and, half waking and half sleeping, he saw a vision.

He saw come past him two horses all beautiful and white, which bore a litter, and in the litter lay a sick knight. When they were near the cross the litter stood still, and Sir Lancelot heard the knight say: "Oh, sweet Lord, when shall this sorrow leave me? And when shall the holy vessel come by, through which I shall be blessed? For I have endured thus long through little trespass."

Thus for some time lamented the knight, and Sir Lancelot heard him.

Then Sir Lancelot saw the candlestick with the six tapers come before the marble cross, and he saw nobody that brought it. Also there came a table of silver and the sacred vessel of the Holy Grail, which Sir Lancelot had seen formerly in King Pelles's house.

Therewith the sick knight sat up, and held up both his hands and prayed to God, and kneeling down, he kissed the holy vessel, and immediately he was whole.

"Lord God, I thank you, for I am healed of this sickness," he said.

So when the Holy Grail had been there a long time, it went into the chapel, with the candlestick and the lights, so that Lancelot did not know what became of it. For he was overmastered by a feeling of his own sinfulness and had no power to rise to follow the holy vessel.

Then the sick knight rose and kissed the cross, and the squire at once brought him his armour and asked his lord how he did.

"Truly, I thank God, right well," he answered. "Through the holy vessel I am healed. But I greatly marvel at this sleeping knight, who had no power to awake when this holy vessel was brought hither."

"I dare right well say," said the squire, "that he dwells in some deadly sin, whereof he has never repented."

"By my faith," said the knight, "whatever he be, he is unhappy, for as I deem he is of the fellowship of the Round Table, which has entered into the Quest of the Holy Grail."

"Sir," said the squire, "here have I brought you all your arms, save your helmet and your sword, and therefore, by my advice you may now take this knight's helmet and his sword."

So the knight did this, and when he was fully armed he took also Sir Lancelot's horse, for it was better than his own. And so he and his attendants departed from the cross.

The Repentance of Sir Lancelot

Straightway Sir Lancelot awoke and sat up, and thought of what he had seen there, and whether it were a dream or not. Right so he heard a voice that said: "Sir Lancelot, more hard than is the stone, and more bitter than is the wood, and more naked and bare than is the leaf of the fig tree! Therefore go you hence and withdraw from this holy place."

When Sir Lancelot heard this, he was passing heavy and knew not what to do, so he rose, sore weeping, and cursed the time that he was born, because he thought he would never more have honour. For those words went to his heart till he knew why he was called so.

He went to fetch his helmet, his sword, and his horse, but found they had all been taken away. Then he called himself wretch and most unhappy of all knights. "My sin and my wickedness have brought me to great dishonour," he said. "For when I sought worldly adventures for worldly desires I ever achieved them, and had the better in every place, and never was I discomfited in any quarrel, were it right or wrong. And now I take upon me the adventures of holy things, but I see and understand that my old sin hinders me and shames, so that I had not power to stir nor speak when the holy vessel appeared before me."

Thus he sorrowed till it was day, and he heard the little birds sing; then he was somewhat comforted.

But when he missed his horse and his arms, Sir Lancelot knew well God was displeased with him. He departed from the cross on foot into the forest, and by dawn came to a high hill, where a hermit dwelt, whom he found just about to begin his morning devotions. Then Lancelot knelt down and cried to the Lord for mercy for his wicked works. When their prayers were over, Lancelot called to the hermit and begged him for charity to hear his life.

"Right willingly," said the good man. "Are you not of King Arthur's court and of the fellowship of the Round Table?"

"Yea, truly, and my name is Sir Lancelot of the Lake, who has been right well spoken of, and now my good fortune is changed, for I am the most wretched man in the world."

The hermit looked at him and marvelled why he was so abashed.

"Sir," said the hermit, "you ought to thank God more than any knight living, for He has caused you to have more worldly worship than any knight that now lives. Because of your presumption to take upon yourself, while you were still in deadly sin, to behold His holy chalice, that was the cause you might not see it with worldly eyes. For He will not appear where such sinners be, except it be to their great hurt and their great shame. And there is no knight living now who ought to give God such thanks as you. For He has given you beauty, seemliness and great strength, above all other knights, and therefore you are the more beholden unto God than any other man, to love Him and dread Him; for your strength and manhood will little avail you if God be against you."

Then Sir Lancelot wept for grief and said: "Now I know well you speak truth to me."

"Sir," said the good man, "hide from me no old sin."

"Truly, I am full loath to reveal it," said Sir Lancelot. "For these fourteen years I have never revealed one thing, and for that I now blame my shame and misadventure."

And then he told that good man all his life, and how he loved a queen beyond all measure, and had done so longer than he could reckon.

"And all my great deeds of arms that I have done, I did the most part for the queen's sake, and for her sake would I do battle, were it right or wrong; and never did I battle only for God's sake, but to win worship and to cause me to be the better beloved; and little or nought I thanked God for it." Then Sir Lancelot said, "I pray you counsel me."

"I will," said the hermit, "if you will assure me that you will never come into the presence of the queen, if you can help it."

Then Sir Lancelot promised him faithfully he would not.

"Look that your heart and your mouth agree," said the good man, "and I will ensure that you shall have more worship than ever you had."

"I marvel at the voice which said to me those strange words I told you of," said Lancelot.

"Have no marvel," said the good man, "for it seems well God loves you. Men can understand a stone is hard by nature, and one kind harder than another—by which is meant *thee*, Sir Lancelot. For you will not leave your sin, for any goodness that God has sent you, therefore are you harder than any stone; and you would never be made soft, neither by water nor by fire—and that is, the Holy Spirit could not enter into you.

"And why that voice called you bitterer than wood—where over-much sin dwells, there can be but little sweetness, wherefore you are likened to an old rotten tree. Now have I shown you why you are harder than the stone, and bitterer than wood.

"Now shall I show you why you are more naked and barer than the fig tree. It befell that our Lord on Palm Sunday preached in Jerusalem, and there He found in the people all hardness, and there He found in all the town not one that would harbour him. Then He went outside the town, and found in the midst of the way a fig tree, which was right fair and well garnished with leaves, but fruit had it none. Then our Lord cursed the tree that bore no fruit—and by the fig tree was betokened Jerusalem, which had leaves and no fruit. So you, Sir Lancelot, when the Holy Grail was brought before you, He found in you no fruit, nor good thought, nor good will; but you were stained with sin."

"Verily," said Sir Lancelot, "all that you have said is true, and from henceforth I purpose by the grace of God never to be so wicked as I have been, but to follow knighthood, and do feats of arms."

Then the good man enjoined Sir Lancelot such penance as he could do, and to follow knighthood; and so he gave him his blessing and prayed Sir Lancelot to abide with him all that day.

"I will gladly," said Sir Lancelot, "for I have neither helmet, nor horse, nor sword."

"As for that," said the good man, "I will help you before tomorrow evening with a horse, and all that belongs to you."

And so Sir Lancelot repented him greatly of all his past misdoings.

The Chamber with the Shut Door

Among the Knights of the Round Table who started on the Quest of the Holy Grail, besides Sir Galahad and Sir Lancelot, the chief were these—the good Sir Percival; Sir Ector de Maris, brother of Sir Lancelot; Sir Bors de Ganis, and Sir Gawaine. Many and strange were the adventures that befell them, and marvellous were the visions they saw, but at no time did they come within sight of the Holy Grail. For except Sir Galahad and Sir Percival, no knight was accounted worthy to behold that divine vision.

But after the penitence of Sir Lancelot, and many long months of wandering, it at last happened to him nearly to achieve the great Quest. For one night being near the sea, a vision came to him in his sleep and bade him enter into the first ship he could find. When he heard these words, he started up and saw a great clearness all round him, so he took his armour and made ready; and when he came to the shore he found a ship without sail or oar. As soon as he was within the ship he felt the greatest sweetness that ever he felt, and a joy that passed all earthly joy that he had ever known. And on this ship he stayed a month or more, sustained by the grace of heaven.

One day there came riding by a knight on horseback, who dismounted when he reached the ship. Then Sir Lancelot found it was his own son, Galahad, and no tongue can tell the joy they made of each other.

They told each other all the adventures and marvels that had befallen them both in many journeys since they departed from King Arthur's court.

Lancelot and Galahad dwelt within that ship half a year, and served God daily and nightly with all their power. And often they arrived in islands far from folk, where nothing but wild beasts were to be found, and they achieved many strange adventures and perilous.

One day it befell that their ship arrived at the edge of a forest, and there they saw a knight armed all in white, richly horsed, and in his right hand he led a white horse. He came to the ship and saluted the two knights, and said: "Galahad, sir, you have been long enough with your father. Come out of the ship, and start upon this horse and go where adventures shall lead you in the Quest of the Holy Grail."

Then Galahad went to his father, and kissed him tenderly and said: "Fair sweet father, I know not when I shall see you more, until I have seen the Holy Grail."

"I pray you," said Lancelot, "pray you to the high Father that He hold me in His service."

So Galahad took his horse, and there they heard a voice that said: "Think to do well, for the one shall never again see the other till the dreadful day of doom."

"Now, son Galahad," said Lancelot, "since we shall part and never see each other more, I pray the high Father to preserve both me and you."

"Sir," said Galahad, "no prayer prevails so much as yours," and therewith he rode away into the forest.

Then the wind arose, and for more than a month drove Lancelot through the sea, where he slept but little, but prayed to God that he might see some tidings of the Holy Grail.

One night, at midnight, he arrived before a castle, which on the back side was rich and fair. A gate opened towards the sea, and it was open without any warders, save that two lions kept the entry, and the moon shone clear.

Then Sir Lancelot heard a voice that said, "Lancelot, go out of this ship and enter into this castle, where you shall see a great part of your desire."

So he ran and armed himself, and came to the gate and saw the lions, and then he set hand to his sword and drew it. But there came a dwarf suddenly and struck him on the arm so sore that the sword fell out of his hand.

"Oh, man of evil faith and poor belief!" he heard a voice say, "wherefore do you trust more in your weapons than in your Maker? For He in whose service you are set might more avail you than your armour."

Then said Lancelot, "I thank You, Lord Christ, for Your great mercy, that You reprove me of my misdeed. Now see I well that You hold me for Your servant."

Then he took his sword again and put it up in his sheath, and signed his forehead with the cross, and came to the lions, and they made semblance to do him harm. Nevertheless, he passed by them without hurt and entered into the castle to the chief fortress, where all the inmates seemed at rest. Then Lancelot, armed as he was, entered in, for he found no gate nor door but it was open. And at the last he found a chamber, the door of which was shut. He set his hand to it to open it, but he could not, although he put forth his utmost force to undo the door.

Then he listened and heard a voice which sang so sweetly that it seemed no earthly thing, and he thought the voice said, "Joy and honour be to the Father of Heaven!"

Then Lancelot knelt down before the chamber door, for he well knew that the Holy Grail was within that chamber, and he prayed to God that if ever he had done anything pleasing in His sight that He would have pity on him and show him something of what he sought.

With that, he saw the chamber door open, and there came out a great clearness, so that the house was as bright as if all the torches of the world had been there. Lancelot went to the door and would have entered, but immediately a voice said: "Flee, Lancelot, and enter not, for you ought not to do so; and if you enter, you shall repent it."

So Lancelot withdrew himself back, right heavy.

Then he looked up into the middle of the chamber, and he saw a table of silver, and the holy vessel covered with red silk, and many angels about it, one of whom held a candle of wax burning. Before the holy vessel he saw a good man clothed as a priest, and it was as if a solemn service were being held. Three men stood near, and it seemed to Lancelot that the priest lifted up the youngest of them, as if to show him to the people. Lancelot marvelled not a little, for he thought that the priest was so burdened with the figure that he would fall to the ground. When he saw no one near would help the priest, Lancelot ran quickly to the door.

"Lord Christ," he said, "take it for no sin, though I help the good man, for he has great need of help."

Right so he entered into the chamber and went towards the table of silver; and when he came nigh, he felt a breath of air as if it were mixed with fire, and it struck him so sore in the face that it seemed to burn him, and therewith he fell to the earth and had no power to rise. Then he felt about him many hands, which took him up and bore him out of the chamber, and left him seemingly dead. And on the morrow he was found by the people of the castle outside the chamber door.

Four-and-twenty days Sir Lancelot lay as if dead, but on the twenty-fifth day he opened his eyes. Then they told him that the castle belonged to King Pelles, where long ago he had seen the vision of the Holy Grail for the first time. All the people marvelled when they found that this stranger was Lancelot, the good knight, and they sent word to King Pelles, who was right glad to hear the news, and went to see him and made great joy of him. And there the king told Lancelot that his fair daughter Elaine, the mother of Galahad, was dead, and Lancelot was grieved to hear the tidings.

Four days Sir Lancelot stayed at the castle, and then he took leave of King Pelles. He knew now that his Quest was ended, for that he would never see more of the Holy Grail than he had seen. So he said he would go back to the realm of Logris, which he had not seen for over a twelvemonth.

When he came to Camelot he found that some of the Knights of the Round Table had returned home, but that many of them—more than half—had been slain and destroyed.

King Arthur, Queen Guinevere and all the court were glad to see Sir Lancelot again, and the king asked him tidings of his son Galahad. Lancelot told the king all the adventures that had befallen him since he departed, and he also told him whatever he knew of the adventures of Galahad, Percival, and Bors.

"Now would to God," said the king, "that they were all three here!"

"That shall never be," said Lancelot, "for two of them shall you never more see. But one of them shall come again."

How Sir Galahad saw the Holy Grail

After leaving Sir Lancelot, Galahad rode many journeys in vain. Wherever he went, strange signs and marvels followed, but not yet did he behold the vision of the Holy Grail.

One day as he rode out of a great forest he was overtaken by Sir Percival, who had followed him for five days, and just afterwards at a crossroads they met Sir Bors. There is no need to tell if they were glad. They told each other their adventures, and all rode on together.

Thus they travelled a great while till they came to the same castle of King Pelles where Sir Lancelot had already been, and directly they entered within the castle King Pelles knew them. Then there was great joy, for all the people knew well by their coming that they had fulfilled the Quest of the Holy Grail.

A little before evening when they were gathered in the hall, a voice was heard among them, and it said, "They that ought not to sit at the table of Jesus Christ arise, for now shall true knights be fed." So everyone went away save King Pelles and Eliazar, his son, who were holy men, and a maid who was his niece. These three and the three knights were left, no more.

Soon they saw nine knights, all armed, come in at the hall door, and take off their helmets and their armour.

"Sir," they said to Galahad, "we have hurried right much to be with you at this table where the holy meat shall be parted."

Then said he, "You are welcome, but from whence come you?"

Three of them said they were from Gaul, and another three said they were from Ireland, and the other three said they were from Denmark.

Then a voice said, "There are two among you who are not in the Quest of the Holy Grail; therefore let them depart." So King Pelles and his son departed.

The knights who remained now saw the table of silver, whereon was the Holy Grail, and it seemed to them that angels stood about it and that a solemn service was being held. They set themselves at the table in great dread and began to pray. Then came One, as it seemed to them, in the likeness of the Lord Christ, and He said: "My knights, and my servants, and my true children, which are come out of deadly life into spiritual life, I will no longer hide from you, but you shall see now a part of My secrets and My hid things. Now hold and receive the high meat which you have so much desired." Then He Himself took the holy vessel and came to Galahad, who knelt down and received the sacred food, and after him, in like manner, all his companions received it; and they thought it so sweet it was marvellous to tell.

Then said He to Galahad, "Son, know you what I hold between My hands?"

"Nay," said he, "unless You will tell me."

"This is," said He, "the holy dish wherein I ate the lamb at the Last Supper. And now have you seen that which you most desired to see, but yet have not seen it so openly as you shall see it in the city of Sarras, in the spiritual place. Therefore you must go hence and bear with you this holy vessel, for this night it shall depart from the realm of Logris and shall never more be seen here. And would you know wherefore? Because these of this land are turned to evil living, therefore I shall disinherit them of the honour which I have done them. Therefore, go you three tomorrow to the sea, where you shall find your ship ready—you and Sir Percival, and Sir Bors, and no more with you. And two of you shall die in My service, but one of you shall go back again to Camelot and bear the tidings."

Then He blessed them and vanished from their sight.

So Galahad, Percival, and Bors left the castle of King Pelles. After riding three days they came to the seashore, where they found the same ship in which Galahad had stayed with Lancelot, and when they went on board they saw in the middle the table of silver and the Holy Grail, which was covered with red silk. Then were they glad to have such things in their fellowship.

So they sailed away till they came to the city of Sarras, where they landed, taking with them the table of silver. As they went in at the gate of the city, they saw sitting there a crooked old man, and Galahad called to him and bade him help them carry the heavy table.

"Truly," said the old man, "for ten years I have not walked except with crutches."

"Never mind," said Galahad, "arise and show your goodwill."

The old man tried to rise, and immediately found himself as whole as ever he had been. Then he ran to the table and took the side opposite Galahad.

The fame of this cure went through the city, and when the king of the city saw the three knights, he asked them whence they came and what thing it was they had brought upon the table of silver. They told him the truth of the Holy Grail, and the power God had placed in it to cure sick people.

The king, however, was a tyrant and came of a line of pagans, and he took the three knights and put them into prison in a deep dungeon. But all the time they were in prison they were supported by the holy grace of heaven.

At a year's end it came to pass that the king lay sick and felt that he should die. Then he sent for the three knights, and when they came before him he begged mercy of them for all that he had done to them, and they willingly forgave him, and so he died.

When the king was dead all the city were dismayed and knew not who could be their king. Right so, as they were in council, came a voice among them and bade them choose the youngest knight of the three to be their king. So they made Galahad king, with the assent of the whole city.

When he had surveyed the country, Galahad caused to be built round the table of silver a chest of gold and of precious stones, which covered the holy vessel, and every morning early the three knights would come before it and say their prayers.

Now at the year's end, on the very day that Galahad was given the crown of gold, he arose up early, he and his companions, and came to the palace, to the holy vessel. There they saw before them a man kneeling, in the likeness of a bishop, and round about him was a great fellowship of angels.

"Come forth, Galahad, servant of Jesus Christ," he said, "and you shall see that which you have long desired to see."

Then Galahad began to tremble, for a vision of spiritual things rose before his earthly eyes, and holding up his hands to heaven, he said: "Lord, I thank You, for now I see that which has been my desire many a day. Now, blessed Lord, I would not longer live, if it might please You, Lord."

Then the good man took the holy food and proffered it to Galahad, and he received it right gladly and meekly.

When this was done, Galahad went to Sir Percival and Sir Bors, and kissed them, and commended them to God. And to Sir Bors he said, "Fair lord, salute me to my lord, Sir Lancelot, my father, and as soon as you see him, bid him be mindful of this unstable world."

Afterwards he knelt down before the table and said his prayers, and suddenly his soul departed to Jesus Christ.

Then it seemed to the two knights that there came a hand from heaven and bore away the holy vessel. And since that time there was never any man so bold as to say he had seen the Holy Grail.

When Percival and Bors saw Galahad dead they made as much sorrow as ever did two men, and if they had not been good men they might easily have fallen into despair. And the people of the city and the country were right heavy. As soon as Galahad was buried, Sir Percival retired to a heritage, and here for a year and two months he lived a full holy life, and then he passed away.

Sir Bors stayed always with Sir Percival as long as he lived, but when he was dead Sir Bors took ship and went back to the realm of Logris, and so came to Camelot, where King Arthur was. Great joy was made of him in the court, for they all thought he must be dead because he had been so long out of the country. Sir Bors told them all the adventures of the Holy Grail, and to Sir Lancelot he gave Galahad's message.

"Sir Lancelot," he said, "Galahad prays you to be mindful of this uncertain world, as you promised him when you were together more than half a year."

"That is true," said Lancelot. "Now I trust to God his prayer shall avail me."

THE DEATH OF ARTHUR

The Departing of Sir Lancelot

After the Quest of the Holy Grail had been fulfilled, and all the knights that were left living were come again to the Round Table, then there was great joy at court, and especially King Arthur and Queen Guinevere rejoiced and were glad because of Sir Lancelot and Sir Bors. And for a time all went well, and there was much feasting and gaiety.

But Sir Lancelot forgot his promise to the good hermit to see as little as possible of Queen Guinevere, and because he was held in such high favour by the king and queen and all the people, some of the other knights were jealous of him and tried to do him all the mischief they could.

Among the knights at King Arthur's court, the most spiteful and malicious was Sir Mordred. He was the youngest son of King Arthur's sister, the wife of King Lot of Orkney, and it was to him that Merlin referred when he prophesied that a child born on May Day should bring destruction to King Arthur. He was half-brother to the noble knights Gawaine, Gaheris, and Gareth, but nothing at all like them in disposition. The only brother who in the least resembled him was Sir Agrivaine, and it was owing to the evil-speaking of these two malicious knights that the storm of anger and misfortune arose, which never ceased till the flower of chivalry of all the world was destroyed and slain.

In the pleasant month of May, when every noble heart glows with life—when earth is looking her sweetest and brightest, and all men and women rejoice and are glad because summer is coming with freshest flowers—in the beautiful month of May, these two knights, Agrivaine and Mordred, set their mischief on foot. In open assembly before many knights they told slanderous tales of Sir Lancelot and Queen Guinevere, and suggested that these should be repeated to the king. Then spoke Sir Gawaine: "Brother Sir Agrivaine," he said, "I pray you and charge you speak no more of such things before me, for know you well, I will not be of your counsel."

"Truly," said Sir Gaheris and Sir Gareth, "we will have nothing to do with your deeds."

"Then I will," said Mordred.

"I well believe that," said Sir Gawaine, "for always, if there is any mischief you will be sharer in it, brother Sir Mordred. I wish you would leave this, and not make yourself such a busybody, for I know what will come of it."

"Come of it what come may," said Sir Agrivaine, "I shall speak to the king."

"Not by my counsel," said Sir Gawaine, "for if there arise war between Sir Lancelot and us, know you well, brother, many kings and great lords will hold with Sir Lancelot. As for my part I will never be against Sir Lancelot, when he rescued me from King Carados of the Dolorous Tower, and slew him and saved my life. Also, brother Agrivaine and Mordred, in like wise Sir Lancelot rescued you both, and three score knights, from Sir Turquine. It seems to me that such good deeds and kindness should be remembered."

"Do as you like," said Sir Agrivaine, "for I will hide it no longer."

At that moment King Arthur came near.

"Now, brother, stay your noise," said Gawaine.

"We will not," said Agrivaine and Mordred.

"Will you not?" said Gawaine, "then God speed you, for I will not hear your tales, nor be of your counsel."

"No more will I," said Sir Gareth and Sir Gaheris, "for we will never speak evil of that man."

And accordingly these three knights left the assembly

"Alas," said Gawaine and Gareth, "now is this realm wholly put in mischief, and the noble fellowship of the Round Table is dispersed."

So, very sorrowfully, they went their way.

King Arthur coming up at that moment asked what the noise was about, whereupon Agrivaine and Mordred were only too ready to repeat their spiteful slander. As the King would scarcely believe what they said, they laid a plot to trap Sir Lancelot. In escaping from this ambush, Sir Lancelot slew Sir Agrivaine and twelve of his companions. Sir Mordred managed to escape, and riding all wounded and bleeding to the king, told him his own version of the story.

"Alas!" said King Arthur, "I sorely repent that ever Sir Lancelot should be against me. Now I am sure the noble fellowship of the Round Table is broken for ever, for with him will hold many a noble knight."

It all fell out as the king and Sir Gawaine had foreseen. From that day there was constant fighting in England, some knights taking part with Sir Lancelot and some with the king, and on both sides many gallant lives were lost. Through sad mischance, the noble knights Sir Gaheris and Sir Gareth, who were unarmed at the time, were accidentally slain by Lancelot's party, after which Sir Gawaine, who had hitherto refused to fight against him, became his most bitter enemy. Many a time the king and Sir Lancelot would have made peace, but it was always Sir Gawaine who urged the king on to fresh fighting and persuaded him not to listen to any attempts at conciliation, although Sir Lancelot made the most noble offers of penitence and expressed the deepest sorrow for the unintentional slaying of Gaheris and Gareth.

At last the Pope sent a command that the fighting should cease, and a stately meeting between the king and Sir Lancelot took place at Carlisle. Here Sir Lancelot spoke such noble words that all the knights and ladies who were present wept to hear him, and the tears fell down King Arthur's cheeks. But the king, to gratify Gawaine's revenge for the loss of his brothers, had already promised that Lancelot should be banished, and now instead of accepting his offer of penitence and goodwill, he allowed Sir Gawaine to declare to Sir Lancelot his doom of exile and that he was forbidden to abide in England more than fifteen days.

Then Sir Lancelot sighed, and the tears fell down his cheeks. "Alas, most noble Christian realm," he said, "whom I have loved above all other realms, in you have I gotten a great part of my honour, and now I shall depart in this way! Truly I repent that ever I came into this realm, that am thus shamefully banished, undeserved and without cause! But fortune is so variant, and the wheel so movable, there is no constant abiding, and that may be proved by many old chronicles, of noble Hector, and Troilus, and Alexander the mighty conqueror, and many others more. When they were highest in their royalty they alighted lowest, and so it fares with me," said Sir Lancelot, "for in this realm I had honour, and by me and the knights of my blood the whole Round Table increased more in renown than by any other."

Then Sir Lancelot bade goodbye to Queen Guinevere in hearing of the king and them all. "Madam," he said, "now I must depart from you and this noble fellowship for ever, and since it is so, I beseech you to pray for me and say me well. And if you be hard bested by any false tongues, my lady, have word sent to me, and if any knight's hands can deliver you by battle, I shall deliver you."

And therewith Sir Lancelot kissed the queen, and then he said all openly: "Now let us see anyone in this place that dare say the queen is not true to my lord Arthur! Let us see who will speak, if he dare speak!"

With that he brought the queen to the king, and then Sir Lancelot took his leave and departed. And there was neither king, duke nor earl, baron or knight, lady or gentlewoman, but all of them wept, as people out of their minds, except Sir Gawaine. And when the noble Sir Lancelot took his horse to ride out of Carlisle, there was sobbing and weeping for pure sorrow at his departing. So he took his way to his Castle of Joyous Gard, and ever after that he called it the Dolorous Gard.

And thus departed Sir Lancelot from the Court of King Arthur for ever.

When Sir Lancelot came to Joyous Gard he called his company of knights together and asked what they would do. They answered all together with one voice that they would do as he did.

"My fair fellows," said Sir Lancelot, "I must depart out of this most noble realm, and now I shall depart it grieves me sore, for I shall depart with no honour. For a banished man never departed out of any realm with any honour, and that is my cause of grief, for ever I fear after many days they will chronicle of me that I was banished out of this land."

Then spoke many noble knights, and said: "Sir, if you are so disposed to abide in this country we will never fail you, and if you do not choose to abide in this land, not one of the good knights here will fail you. Since it pleased us to take part with your distress and heaviness in this realm, know you well, it shall equally please us to go into other countries with you, and there to take such part as you do."

"My fair lords," said Lancelot, "I well understand you, and as I can, thank you. And you shall understand that such livelihood as I am born to, I will give up to you, in this manner—namely, I will share all my livelihood and all my lands freely among you, and I myself will have as little as any of you, and I trust to God to maintain you on my lands as well as ever were maintained any knights."

Then spoke all the knights at once: "Shame on him that will leave you! For we all understand that in this realm will now be no quiet, but always strife and debate, now the fellowship of the Round Table is broken. For by the noble fellowship of the Round Table was King Arthur borne up, and by their nobleness the king and all his realm were in quiet and in rest. And a great part, everyone said, was because of your nobleness."

"Truly," said Sir Lancelot, "I thank you all for your good words, though I know well all the stability of this realm was not due to me. But as far as I could I did my duty, and some rebellions in my days were appeased by me. And I trow we shall soon hear of them again, and that is what grieves me sorely. For ever I dread that Sir Mordred will make trouble, for he is passing envious and applies himself to mischief."

So all the knights were agreed to go with Sir Lancelot, and quite a hundred departed with him and made their vows they would never leave him, for well or ill.

So they shipped at Cardiff and sailed to Bayonne in France, where Sir Lancelot was lord of many lands.

The Vengeance of Sir Gawaine

Not content with having banished Sir Lancelot, King Arthur and Sir Gawaine made a great host ready and prepared to follow him, taking ship at Cardiff. During his absence King Arthur appointed his nephew Sir Mordred to be chief ruler of all England and put Queen Guinevere under his charge. So he passed over the sea and landed on Sir Lancelot's lands, and there, through the vengeance of Sir Gawaine, he burnt and wasted all that they could overrun.

When word was brought to Sir Lancelot that King Arthur and Sir Gawaine were landed and destroying all his possessions, his knights urged him to go forth to battle, but he replied that he was full loath to ride out to shed Christian blood, so first he would send a message to King Arthur to see if a treaty could be made, for peace was always better than war. So Lancelot sent forth a damsel to King Arthur, demanding that he should cease warring against his lands.

The damsel started on her horse, and when she came to the pavilion of King Arthur she alighted; and there met a gentle knight, Sir Lucas the butler.

"Fair damsel, do you come from Sir Lancelot of the Lake?"

"Yes, sir," she said, "I come hither to speak with my lord the king."

"Alas," said Sir Lucas, "my lord would love Lancelot, but Sir Gawaine will not let him." And then he added, "I pray to God, damsel, you may fare well, for all we that are about the king would that Sir Lancelot did best of any knight living."

With this, Lucas led the damsel to King Arthur, where he sat with Sir Gawaine, to hear what she would say. When she had told her tale, tears filled the king's eyes, and all the lords were full glad to advise the king to be reconciled with Sir Lancelot, save only Sir Gawaine.

"My lord, my uncle, what will you do?" he said. "Will you turn back again now that you have come thus far on this journey? All the world will speak scorn of you."

"Nay," said King Arthur, "you know well, Sir Gawaine, I will do as you advise me; and yet it seems to me it were not good to refuse his fair proffers. But since I am come so far upon this journey, I will that you give the damsel her answer, for I cannot speak to her for pity, her proffers are so generous."

Then Sir Gawaine said to the damsel thus: "Damsel, say you to Sir Lancelot that it is waste labour now to sue to my uncle. For tell him if he would have made any attempt at peace, he should have made it before this time, for tell him now it is too late. And say that I, Sir Gawaine, so send him word that I promise him by the faith I owe to God and to knighthood, I shall never leave Sir Lancelot till he have slain me, or I him."

So the damsel wept and departed, and there were many weeping eyes. She came back to Sir Lancelot, where he was among all his knights, and when Sir Lancelot heard this answer then the tears ran down his cheeks.

Then his noble knights strode about him and said, "Sir Lancelot, wherefore make you such cheer? Think what you are, and what men we are, and let us noble men match them in midst of the field."

"That may easily be done," said Lancelot, "but I was never so loath to do battle, for I will always avoid that noble king who made me knight. When I can keep quiet no longer, I must needs defend myself, and that will be more honour for me, and for us all, than to strive with that noble king whom we have all served."

Then they spoke no more, and as it was night, went to rest.

On the morrow early, in the dawning of the day, as the knights looked out, they saw the city of Bayonne besieged round about, and ladders were fast being set up. Then from the town they defied King Arthur's host, and beat them from the walls mightily. So the siege went on for six months, and there was much slaughter of people on both sides. Then one day that Sir Gawaine came before the gates, armed at all points, on a noble horse, with a great spear in his hand.

"Where are you now, you false traitor, Sir Lancelot?" he cried with a loud voice. "Why hide you within holes and walls, like a coward? Look out, now, you false traitor knight, and here I shall revenge upon your body the death of my three brethren."

Every word of this was heard by Sir Lancelot and all his knights, and now there was nothing to be done but for Sir Lancelot to defend himself, or else to be coward for ever. Sir Lancelot bade saddle his strongest horse, and fetch his arms and bring them all to the gate of the tower, and then he spoke aloud to King Arthur: "My lord Arthur, and noble king who made me knight, know well I am right heavy for your sake that you pursue me thus, and always I forbear you, for if I had been revengeful, I might have met you in open field, there to have made your boldest knights full tame. Now I have forborne half a year, and suffered you and Sir Gawaine to do what you would do, and now I can endure it no longer—now I must needs defend myself, inasmuch as Sir Gawaine has accused me of treason. It is greatly against my will that ever I should fight against any of your blood. But now I cannot resist it, I am driven to it, as a beast to bay."

"Sir Lancelot," cried Gawaine, "if you dare do battle, leave your babbling and come away, and let us ease our hearts."

King Arthur's host outside the city stood still, all apart, and Lancelot's noble knights came out in a great number, insomuch that when King Arthur saw the multitude of men and knights he marvelled and said to himself: "Alas, that ever Sir Lancelot was against me, for now I see he has borne with me!"

So the covenant was made that no man should go near Lancelot and Gawaine, or have anything to do with them till the one was dead or yielded.

Now, years ago, a holy man had given a strange gift and favour to Sir Gawaine, which no one knew of except King Arthur. Every day in the year, from nine o'clock in the morning till high noon, his might increased three times its usual strength. The king appointed most trials of arms to take place at this time of day, which caused Sir Gawaine to win great honour.

Thus Sir Lancelot fought with Sir Gawaine, and when he felt his strength evermore increase, Lancelot wondered, and sorely dreaded to be ashamed. But when it was past noon Sir Gawaine had nothing but his own strength to rely on, and then Lancelot felt him grow weaker. Then he doubled his strokes, and gave Sir Gawaine such a blow on the helmet that he fell down on his side, and Lancelot withdrew himself from him.

"Why withdraw you?" said Sir Gawaine. "Now turn again, false traitor knight, and slay me. For if you leave me thus, when I am whole I shall do battle with you again."

"I shall endure you, sir, by God's grace," replied Sir Lancelot, "but know you well, Sir Gawaine, I will never strike a felled knight."

So Sir Lancelot went back into the city, and Sir Gawaine was borne into one of King Arthur's pavilions, where doctors came to him and dressed his wounds.

Then King Arthur fell sick for sorrow because Sir Gawaine was so sorely hurt, and because of the war between him and Sir Lancelot. Those of King Arthur's party kept the siege with little fighting outside, and those within guarded their walls and defended them when need was.

Sir Gawaine lay sick in his tent for about three weeks, and as soon as he could ride he once more came before the chief gate of Bayonne and challenged Lancelot to fight. And once more Lancelot wounded him sorely and struck him down.

"Traitor knight," cried Sir Gawaine, "know well, I am not yet slain. Come near me and perform this battle to the utmost."

"I will do no more than I have done," said Sir Lancelot, "for when I see you on foot, I will do battle against you all the while I see you stand on your feet; but to strike a wounded man that cannot stand, God defend me from such shame!" And then he turned and went his way towards the city.

"Sir Lancelot, when I am whole I shall do battle with you again," Sir Gawaine called out after him, "for I shall never leave you till one of us is slain."

So the siege went on, and Sir Gawaine lay sick nearly a month. And when he was well recovered and ready within three days to do battle again with Sir Lancelot, tidings came to King Arthur from England, which made the king and all his host remove.

The Battle in the West

While King Arthur was away in France, Mordred, who had been appointed ruler of England, was busy about his own wicked plots. He now forged letters, as though they came from beyond the sea, and the letters specified that King Arthur had been slain in battle with Sir Lancelot. Mordred thereupon summoned a parliament, and calling the lords together, he made them choose him king, so he was crowned at Canterbury and held a feast there fifteen days. Afterwards he withdrew to Camelot, and sent for Queen Guinevere and told her plainly that he wished to marry her. Everything was made ready for the feast, and the day for the wedding was fixed.

Queen Guinevere was in great distress, but she did not dare oppose Sir Mordred openly, and therefore she pretended to agree. Then she asked leave to go to London to buy all manner of things necessary for the wedding. Because of her fair words, Sir Mordred trusted her well enough and gave her leave to go.

Directly she reached London, Queen Guinevere at once seized the Tower, and in all haste possible stuffed it with all manner of victuals and well garrisoned it with men, and so kept it.

When Mordred found he had been outwitted he was angry beyond measure. He went and laid a mighty siege to the Tower of London, and assaulted it with great engines and guns, but he could not prevail. He tried in all ways, by letters and messages, to make Queen Guinevere come out of the Tower, but it availed nothing; neither for fair words nor foul would the queen trust herself again in the traitor's hands. She answered shortly that she would rather slay herself than marry him.

Then word came to Mordred that King Arthur had raised the siege on Sir Lancelot and was coming home with a great host to be avenged on his nephew. Mordred accordingly sent writs to all the barony of England, and numbers of people flocked to him. For it was a common report among them that with Arthur was no other life but war and strife, and with Mordred was great joy and bliss. Thus was King Arthur maligned and evil spoken of. And there were many whom King Arthur had raised up from nothing, and given lands to, who could not now say of him a good word.

So Sir Mordred marched with a large host to Dover, and there came King Arthur with a great navy of ships and galleys, while Mordred waited ready to prevent his landing. Then there was launching of big boats and small, full of noble men of arms, and there was much slaughter of gentle knights, and many a bold baron on both sides was laid low. But King Arthur was so courageous, no manner of men could prevent his landing, and his knights fiercely followed him. They drove Mordred back, and he fled, and all his army.

After the battle was over, King Arthur buried his people that were slain, and then the noble knight Sir Gawaine was found in a boat, lying more than half dead. He had been hurt again on the wound which Sir Lancelot had given him at Bayonne, and now he must die.

"Alas, Sir Gawaine," said the king, "here now you lie, the man in the world whom I loved the most, and now is my joy gone! In Sir Lancelot and you I had most joy, and now have I lost you both."

"Mine uncle, King Arthur," said Gawaine, "know you well, my death day is come, and all is through my own hastiness and wilfulness. Had Sir Lancelot been with you as he used to be, this unhappy war had never begun, and of all this am I the cause. For Sir Lancelot and his kindred through their prowess held all your enemies in subjection and danger, and now you shall miss Sir Lancelot. But alas, I would not agree with him, and therefore I pray you let me have paper, pen, and ink that I may write to Sir Lancelot a letter with my own hand."

Then Sir Gawaine wrote a letter to Sir Lancelot, "flower of all noble knights", telling him all that had happened, and how he had brought his death on himself because he was hurt on the same wound that Lancelot had given him at Bayonne.

"Also, Sir Lancelot," he went on, "for all the love that ever was between us, make no tarrying, but come over the sea in all haste that you may with your gallant knights rescue the noble king who made you knight, that is my lord Arthur, for he is full straitly bested with a false traitor, my half-brother, Sir Mordred."

Then Sir Gawaine bade King Arthur send for Lancelot and cherish him above all other knights, and so, at the hour of noon, Sir Gawaine yielded up the spirit.

After this, King Arthur fought again with Sir Mordred and drove him westward across England, towards Salisbury, where a day was appointed for the king to meet Sir Mordred in battle on a down near Salisbury, not far from the sea.

The night before the battle, King Arthur dreamed a wonderful dream. It seemed to him he sat on a platform, in a chair, clad in the richest cloth of gold that could be made; and the chair was fast to a wheel. And the king thought that under him, far from him, was a hideous deep black water, and therein were all manner of serpents, and worms, and wild beasts, foul and horrible. And suddenly, the king thought, the wheel turned upside down, and he fell among the serpents, and every beast seized him by a limb.

Then the king cried as he lay in his bed—"Help!" And knights, squires and yeomen ran to the king and wakened him, and he was so amazed he did not know where he was.

Then he fell slumbering again, not sleeping, nor thoroughly wakening. And it seemed to him that Sir Gawaine came to him and warned him not to fight with Sir Mordred on the morrow, for if he did so he would certainly die. Sir Gawaine counselled him to make a treaty for a month, for within that time Sir Lancelot would come with all his noble knights and would rescue King Arthur, and slay Sir Mordred.

Then Sir Gawaine vanished.

Directly King Arthur awoke he sent for all his wise lords and bishops, and told them his vision and of Sir Gawaine's warning. They went at once to Sir Mordred and made a treaty, promising him that while King Arthur lived he should have Cornwall and Kent, and after the king's death, the whole of England. It was further agreed that a meeting between King Arthur and Mordred should take place between the two armies, and each of them should take fourteen persons.

King Arthur, on starting for this meeting, warned all his army that if they saw any sword drawn they were to come on fiercely and slay the traitor Mordred, for he in no way trusted him. And in like manner Sir Mordred also warned his host.

So they met, as had been appointed, and they were agreed and thoroughly in accordance. Wine was fetched, and they drank.

Just at that moment came an adder out of a little heath bush, and it stung a knight on the foot. When the knight felt himself stung, he looked down and saw the adder. Then he drew his sword to slay the adder and thought of no other harm.

But when the host on both sides saw that sword drawn, then they blew bugles and trumpets and horns and shouted grimly. So both the armies rushed to arms, and never was seen a more doleful battle in any Christian land.

All that day long they fought without ceasing, and when night came, of all King Arthur's noble knights there were none left alive but Sir Lucas the butler, and his brother Sir Bedivere, and both were sorely wounded. Then was King Arthur angry out of measure when he saw his people so slain from him.

"Alas, that ever I should see this doleful day! For now I am come to my end," said Arthur. "But would to God I knew where that traitor Sir Mordred is, who has caused all this mischief."

Then was King Arthur aware where Sir Mordred leaned on his sword among a great heap of dead men. Sir Lucas tried to persuade the king not to fight with Mordred, reminding of Sir Gawaine's warning.

"Blessed be God, you have won the field," he said, "for here we are three alive, and with Sir Mordred there are none living. And if you leave off now, this wicked day of destiny is past."

"Tide me death, betide me life " said the king, "now I see him yonder alone, he shall never escape my hands, for at a better advantage I shall never have him."

"God speed you well!" said Sir Bedivere.

Then King Arthur took his spear in both hands, and ran towards Mordred, crying: "Traitor, now is your death day come!"

When Sir Mordred heard King Arthur he ran at him with his sword drawn. Then King Arthur thrust Mordred through the body with his spear so that he fell dead, but Mordred's sword pierced the helmet and brain pan of King Arthur that he fell in a swoon to the earth.

"The Noblest Knight of the World"

Sir Lucas and Sir Bedivere lifted up King Arthur and carried him to a little chapel not far from the seashore, but Sir Lucas was so grievously wounded that he fell dead before they could go to a further place of safety. Sir Bedivere wept for the death of his brother, but the king bade him stay his mourning, for his own life was hurrying fast away.

"Therefore," said Arthur, "take Excalibur, my good sword, and go with it to yonder waterside; and when you get there throw my sword in the water, and come again and tell me what you there see."

"My lord," said Bedivere, "your commandment shall be done, and I will quickly bring you word again."

So Bedivere departed, and by the way he beheld that noble sword, how that the pommel and the hilt were all of precious stones. Then he said to himself, "If I throw this rich sword in the water, good will never come of it, but harm and loss."

So Sir Bedivere hid Excalibur under a tree and went back to the king as quickly as he could, and said he had been at the water and thrown in the sword.

"What saw you there?" said the king.

"Sir," he said, "I saw nothing but waves and winds."

"That is untruly said," spoke the king. "Therefore go you quickly again and do my command as you are lief and dear to me. Spare not, but throw it in."

Then Bedivere went back and took the sword in his hand; and then it seemed a sin and shame to throw away that noble sword; so again he hid the sword, and returned to Arthur and told him he had done his command.

"What saw you there?" said the king.

"Sir," he said, "I saw nothing but the ripple of water and lapping of the waves."

"Ah, traitor, untrue!" cried King Arthur, "now have you betrayed me twice. Who would have thought that you who have been to me so lief and dear, and you who are named a noble knight, would betray me for the riches of the sword! But now go again quickly, for your long tarrying puts me in great jeopardy of my life."

Then Sir Bedivere departed and fetched the sword, and taking it to the waterside, he bound the girdle about the hilt and threw the sword as far into the water as he could. Then came an arm and a hand above the water, and met it and caught it, and so shook it thrice and brandished it, and then the hand with the sword vanished away in the water. So Sir Bedivere came again to the king and told him what he had seen.

"Alas," said the king, "help me hence, for I dread I have tarried overlong."

Then Sir Bedivere took the king upon his back and carried him to the waterside. And when they reached it, a barge drifted in quite close to the bank, with many fair ladies in it. They had all black hoods, and they wept and cried when they saw King Arthur.

"Now put me into the barge," said the king, and Sir Bedivere did so, softly.

And there received him three queens, with great mourning, and so they set him down, and King Arthur laid his head in the lap of one of the queens.

"Ah, dear brother," she said, "why have you tarried so long from me?"

Then they rowed from the land, and Sir Bedivere beheld them go from him.

"Ah, my lord Arthur," he cried, "what shall become of me now you go from me and leave me here alone among my enemies?"

"Comfort yourself," said the king, "and do as well as you can, for in me is no trust to trust in. For I go to the vale of Avilion, to heal me of my grievous wound. And if you hear never more of me, pray for my soul."

Thus King Arthur was borne away in the barge with the three queens—the one was King Arthur's sister, Morgan le Fay, another was the queen of North Wales, the third was the queen of the Waste Lands. Also in the barge was Nimue, the chief Lady of the Lake, and this lady had done much for King Arthur.

And some people say that King Arthur died, and that the three queens took his body to a little hermitage near Glastonbury, but many think that King Arthur never died at all but dwells now in some beautiful valley of rest, and that one day he will come again to rule over England. For on his tomb this verse is written: "Here lies Arthur, king that was, and king that shall be."

When news came to Queen Guinevere that King Arthur was slain, and all the noble knights, and Sir Mordred, she stole away with five ladies to Amesbury. There she took refuge in a convent and spent the rest of her days in fasting, prayers and alms deeds.

In the meanwhile, Sir Lancelot had received Sir Gawaine's letter, and with all the haste he hurried back to England with his company of noble knights. But when they arrived they found they were too late; King Arthur and Sir Mordred were both slain. Sir Lancelot thereupon rode in search of Queen Guinevere, and at last he found her in the nunnery at Amesbury. The queen told him that she intended never to come out again into the world, and when Lancelot heard this, he determined also to retire to a hermitage.

Taking his horse he rode away into a great forest, and so it chanced he came to the little chapel near Glastonbury where the body of King Arthur had been buried. Sir Bedivere was still there, and Sir Lancelot asked the good bishop who was hermit if he might remain. Here Sir Bors followed him, and others of his noble knights, who when they found Sir Lancelot had taken himself to such holiness, had no desire to depart. Thus for six years they lived a life of penance, paying no regard to worldly riches and caring nothing what pain they endured, when they saw the noblest knight of the world suffer such hardship.

Sir Lancelot had lived in the hermitage about seven years when one night a vision came to him, bidding him hasten to Amesbury, for there he would find Queen Guinevere dead. And Lancelot was told to take a horse bier and go with his fellow knights to fetch the body of Queen Guinevere, and bury her by her husband, the noble King Arthur.

So all was done as the vision commanded, and Queen Guinevere was brought from Amesbury to Glastonbury with much sorrow and splendour. A hundred torches were kept burning round the bier, and Lancelot and seven of his knights walked always round it, singing, and saying holy prayers, and strewing frankincense. Thus they came from Amesbury to Glastonbury, and on the morrow Queen Guinevere was buried in the little chapel, in the tomb of King Arthur.

When the coffin was put into the earth, Sir Lancelot swooned and lay for a long time still, till the good bishop, who was hermit, came out and awaked him.

"You be to blame," he said, "for you displease God with such manner of sorrow-making."

"Truly," said Sir Lancelot, "I trust I do not displease God, for He knows my intent. My sorrow was not, and is not, from any sinful cause, but my sorrow can never have an end. For when I remember the beauty of the queen, and the nobleness that was with her and the king—and when I saw them thus lie here together dead—truly my heart would not serve to sustain me. Also, when I remember how by my fault, my arrogance and my pride, they were both laid low, who were peerless of any Christian people, know you well," said Sir Lancelot, "this remembrance of their kindness and my unkindness sank so to my heart, that I could not sustain myself."

After this, Sir Lancelot fell ill, eating and drinking little, and gradually pining away, for there was nothing anyone could do to comfort him. Evermore, day and night he prayed, but sometimes he slumbered a broken sleep, and often he was found lying on the tomb of King Arthur and Queen Guinevere. At last he grew so weak that he could no longer rise from bed, and then he sent for the good bishop and all his faithful companions, and begged that he might receive the last sacred rites of religion. When all had been done in due order, he prayed the bishop that when he was dead his comrades might bear his body to his own Castle of Joyous Gard, for there he had sworn a vow he would be buried.

Then there was weeping and wringing of hands among his fellow knights.

That night, while all lay asleep, the good bishop had a beautiful dream. He thought he saw Sir Lancelot surrounded with a great throng of angels, and they carried him up to heaven, and the gates of heaven were opened to him.

"It is but a dream," said Sir Bors. "I doubt not nothing but good ails Sir Lancelot."

"That may well be," said the bishop. "But go you to his bed, and then we shall prove the truth."

When Sir Bors and the other knights came to Sir Lancelot's bed, they found him dead, and he lay as if he smiled, and all around him there was the sweetest fragrance that ever they smelt.

On the morrow, after chanting the Requiem Mass, the bishop and the knights put Sir Lancelot in the same horse bier in which Queen Guinevere had been brought to Glastonbury, and took him to his own Castle of Joyous Gard, and they had always a hundred torches burning about him; and so within fifteen days they came to Joyous Gard. There they laid him in the body of the choir, and sang and read many prayers and psalms over him; and his face was left uncovered that all folk might see him, for such was the custom in those days.

And right thus, as they were at their service, came Sir Ector de Maris, who for seven years had sought all England, Scotland, and Wales for his brother Lancelot. When he heard the noise and saw the choir of Joyous Gard all lighted up, he dismounted from his horse and came into the choir, and there he saw men singing and weeping. And they all knew Sir Ector, but he did not know them. Then Sir Bors went to Sir Ector and told him how there lay his brother, Sir Lancelot, dead. Sir Ector threw his shield, sword, and helmet from him, and when he beheld Sir Lancelot's face, it were hard for any tongue to tell the doleful complaints that he made for his brother.

"Ah, Lancelot," he said, "you were head of all Christian knights. And now, I dare say," said Sir Ector, "you, Sir Lancelot, there you lie, that you were never matched of earthly knight's hand; and you were the courtliest knight that ever bore shield; and you were the truest friend to your lover that ever bestrode horse; and you were the truest lover of any sinful man that ever loved woman; and you were the kindest man that ever struck with sword; and you were the goodliest person that ever came among press of knights; and you were the meekest man and the gentlest that ever ate in hall among ladies; and you were the sternest knight to your mortal foe that ever put spear in the rest."

Then there was weeping and grief out of measure.

THE END